We kept crawling up the slope. I understood that if we reached a certain height before the guard turned around, he wouldn't be as likely to spot us.

Mother wasn't crawling as fast as I could have. I heard her labored breathing. I kept looking over my shoulder at the guard, still with his back to us.

Suddenly, my right arm sank into a deep hole, stopping only when my face pressed against the packed snow. I tried to pull out my arm, but something under the snow held it. Terror gripped me.

ESCAPING THE HOLOCAUST

A TRUE STORY

ESCAPING THE HOLOCAUST

A TRUE STORY

JULIAN PADOWICZ

Scholastic Inc.

ISBN 978-0-545-51570-2

Copyright © 2013 by Julian Padowicz

All rights reserved. Published by Scholastic Inc., 557 Broadway, New York, NY 10012, by arrangement with Academy Chicago Publishers. SCHOLASTIC and associated logos are trademarks and/or registered trademarks of Scholastic Inc.

12 11 10 9 8 7 6 5 4 3 2   13 14 15 16 17 18/0

Printed in the U.S.A.   40
First Scholastic printing, October 2013

This book is lovingly dedicated to the memory of my late wife,
Phyllis McKenny Padowicz,
who devoted her life to the education of young people.
— J.P.

CHAPTER 1

The truck stopped as though it had hit something, and I almost tumbled to the floor. Mr. Dembowski, our driver, opened the door and yelled, "Everybody under the truck!"

"Get the children out of the truck!" someone else yelled as we scrambled to get out.

Our driver grabbed me by the waist and yanked me to the ground.

Mother grabbed my hand. "Run, Yulian!" she yelled, pulling me along. (*YU-lee-an* is how my name is pronounced in Polish.)

"Under the truck!" Mr. Dembowski shouted. We crawled under the truck bed, and I had no idea what was happening.

Then came the sound of airplanes—not the faint hum of a plane above the clouds, but the roar of fast-approaching aircraft. It was a sound I had never heard before, but there was no mistaking it. My mother was on top of me under the truck. I raised my head to see, but she pushed it down again.

I heard a blast of air and the roar of engines, feeling it with my body and sensing the truck swaying over us. "Stay down!" Mr. Dembowski shouted. The roar grew fainter and then stopped. I heard nothing except my labored breathing as I tried to change position.

I wanted to see the planes. I had never seen one up close, and I guessed these must have passed near enough to see the pilots in their cockpits. I was seven years old, and this was important to me.

Then I heard the sound again. First a hum, then a growing roar. Mother's arm pushed my head down again. Now there was a new sound, which I had no trouble identifying. Machine-gun fire.

The noises were terrible: metal tearing and people screaming.

The shrieks of the planes and the creaking of the truck blew over us one more time, and then it was still.

"Stay down. Everybody stay down," Mr. Dembowski said.

We lay still, surrounded by the sounds of crying people and dying animals.

The attack had occurred only a few months ago, when the Nazis invaded our country in September 1939. So much had happened to us since then. Now it was February, and Mother and I were sitting in a train compartment, disguised as peasants on the first stage of Mother's escape attempt from Poland. Mother had been told that her plan was crazy. Now we were hoping desperately that the real peasant, sitting across from us in his knee-high boots, would not see through our disguise.

CHAPTER 2

We had been warned that war might come. My nanny, Kiki, and I had been to the police station to be issued gas masks, because in the last war the Germans had used poison gas. Now the Germans were talking about declaring war on Poland again. Kiki and I were living in Warsaw, the capital of Poland, along with my mother, Barbara; my stepfather, Lolek; and our cook, Marta. Kiki, who remembered the previous war, said that we should always keep our gas masks with us, day and night.

On September 1, we heard on the radio that German

tanks and airplanes had crossed our western border and were pushing toward Warsaw without declaring war. Taken by surprise, our Polish soldiers, on foot and on horseback, were trying to hold the Germans back, but they were greatly outnumbered.

The radio also said that more troops were being rushed to reinforce them and that civilians who were in the army reserves were being called up. Lolek, who was a reserve officer, had put on his uniform that morning and left our apartment to report to headquarters. I hadn't seen him since.

Suddenly, the radio announced an air raid on Warsaw. Sirens blared, and the four of us—Mother, Kiki, Marta, and I—went to sit in our entrance hall, the one room without windows in our apartment.

Mother asked Kiki to tell us all a story while we sat out the air raid. We heard popping sounds outside, which grew into booms that shook our building. One bomb hit so close that Marta's chair collapsed under her. I started to laugh when I saw Marta on her knees holding a broken-off chair leg in her hand, but Kiki gave me a look that said this was no laughing matter. Luckily, the air raid ended soon after that.

Kiki and I didn't go to the park that day, as we normally would, and my mother didn't leave the apartment, either. She spent a lot of time on the phone.

That evening, after she heard me say my prayers, Kiki hugged me a little longer than usual and reminded me to say my prayers that same way every night. She told me that I should love my mother more than anyone else in the world.

I understood why she was saying these things. Kiki had explained to me that in the last war, many people who weren't even soldiers had been killed. If that were to happen to us, I should be ready to be accepted into heaven by living a good life, believing in Jesus with all my heart, and reciting my prayers regularly.

I was Jewish, not Catholic like Kiki. But she said that God could overlook that technicality and consider me a Catholic at heart on the strength of my strong belief and my prayers. Heaven, Kiki said, was open only to Catholics.

She taught me to recite the Our Father and the Hail Mary, to make the sign of the cross, and to say the Rosary. I had come to believe that my Jewish mother and stepfather would not be allowed into heaven, but it was Kiki who was most important to me. My mother and stepfather traveled a lot and were busy with a great many things, so I saw them only rarely.

That evening, Kiki also told me that I was a little soldier, and that little soldiers did not cry. I assured her I would remember that.

When I woke the following morning, Kiki was gone. Her bedding was stripped, and the crucifix on her wall was gone. My heart was gripped by panic, but I remembered her admonishment about being a little soldier and did not cry.

CHAPTER 3

Marta made breakfast for me in the kitchen, but I couldn't eat. I felt hollow inside. And it hurt.

I had felt that hollow before, when Kiki sometimes took a day off. The moment the front door closed after her, I would feel it and start to cry. Mother would try to distract me, but it wouldn't do any good. She would try telling me stories the way Kiki did, but she didn't know them well and would get them wrong. She ended up calling one of her friends, and the two of them would take me to a café, where I could eat cheesecake while they drank coffee and talked about dresses or people they knew. But the pain was much bigger this time, because I knew Kiki wasn't coming back.

Mother was known as Beautiful Basia. People said she was one of the most gorgeous women in Warsaw. She had a round face and large brown eyes. She always dressed in the latest style, and had her hair done weekly.

My real father had died when I was a year old, and I did not remember him. Lolek, my stepfather, was tall, and he and Mother had a great many friends. When they weren't traveling, Mother and Lolek were invited to cocktail or dinner parties. When Kiki took her day off and Mother tried to cheer me up, it was almost like being with a stranger. I knew Kiki and Marta better than I knew Mother.

There was another air raid that morning. As Mother, Marta, and I sat in our apartment hallway again, I could see them tense up every time a bomb exploded nearby. I almost wished that one would come crashing right into our hallway and blow us up, so I could go to heaven where nobody ever got hurt or felt bad. Then I could just wait for Kiki to join me.

Mother told me that we were going to leave Warsaw that night with Aunt Edna and my cousin Fredek to stay in the countryside, where the Germans weren't bombing. We would stay there until the war was over. I thought she expected me to brighten at the thought of going with Fredek, but I didn't like Fredek very much. He was six months younger than me, but when we played together, he always wanted to play war, and I had to be wounded, taken prisoner, or killed. He was always the hero.

Mother also told me that Kiki would be joining us there in a few days. But when I asked where in the country, she said they hadn't decided yet. If they hadn't yet decided where yet, how could Kiki have agreed to meet us there?

There was a second air raid that afternoon, and the explosions were even closer. After supper, Mother and I said good-bye to Marta and took a doroszka [dor-osh-kah] to Aunt Edna's apartment. Doroszkas were horse-drawn taxis, the only kind of taxi available now in Warsaw, since all the automobiles had been taken by the army for troop transportation.

It took us a long time to reach Aunt Edna's apartment because many streets were blocked by bombed buildings. By the time we arrived, it was late, and Aunt Edna said she had been worried that something had happened to us.

Suddenly, a woman I had never seen before

approached us. She spoke to me, not to Mother, and said that her name was Miss Bronia. She mentioned that she knew Kiki. And said she knew how upset I must be. She took my hand and led me to cousin Fredek's room, where Fredek was already asleep on his bed with his clothes on. Somebody else was lying on the other bed, which belonged to Fredek's nanny.

Miss Bronia told me to take off my shoes, lie down next to Fredek, and try to sleep. She didn't tell me to go to sleep, as Mother would have, but only to try, because she knew it wouldn't be easy. I must have fallen right asleep, wondering what the next day would bring.

CHAPTER 4

The next thing I knew, I woke up in a blanket, sitting with my back against a wall. It was dark except for the tiny amount of light coming in through an open door. The upper half of a man was in the doorway, and I realized I was in the back of a closed truck. Somebody, probably the driver, had just opened the door from the outside.

"The road is blocked, Mrs. Waisbrem," he said, addressing my mother. "There's a car . . ." he began, but didn't finish. I knew that meant something bad had happened.

"I want to see!" said Fredek, rushing past me.

"Fredek, where are you going?" Aunt Edna called after him from the darkness.

"I'll go with him, Mrs. Tiszman," Miss Bronia said. I was relieved to hear that she had come with us. The driver helped Miss Bronia down, and she went after Fredek.

Now I could make out Mother, Aunt Edna, and another woman sitting on a bench on the other side of the truck. On the floor between us were suitcases and boxes. On the opposite end of my bench, wrapped in a blanket and still asleep, was one more person.

Looking out the open door, I saw that it was gray outside, the way it got just before dawn. The road behind our truck was full of people traveling on foot and in wagons. Some people were on bicycles; others pushed wheelbarrows and baby carriages. Some of the wagons were piled with furniture, and I wasn't sure what was in the baby carriages. The people on foot were moving slowly past us. The people in wagons couldn't pass and were standing still.

"I need some fresh air," Aunt Edna said, going to the open door. "My God, what are all those people doing?" she said.

"They're trying to get away from the bombs," said the woman I didn't recognize. I realized that she must be Aunt Edna's sister-in-law, whom I knew as Aunt Paula; that the mysterious person wrapped in the blanket must be her daughter, Sonya, Fredek's older cousin; and that Miss Bronia must be Sonya's nanny.

"They're trying to get away from the bombs, just like us," Aunt Paula said.

"Fredek's down there," Aunt Edna said. I could hear the worry in her voice.

"He'll be all right," Aunt Paula reassured her. "Bronia's with him."

"I'd better look."

Our driver helped Aunt Edna down from the truck. The other two mothers followed. Left alone in the truck, except for Sonya, who was still asleep, I decided to go outside, too. The driver lifted me and set me on the ground.

I heard a soft murmuring and saw a horse's muzzle close enough to touch. I reached out a hand, palm up, the way my grandfather's coachman had shown me to do, so the horse wouldn't nip me. The horse nibbled gently at my palm. I reached with my other hand for the front of his neck, which I knew would be soft. I petted it.

"Yulian, get away from that horse!" I heard my mother yell. "He'll kick you."

I knew that horses could only kick someone

standing behind them. But I didn't want to argue. I gave his nose one more pat and stepped around our truck to see what was blocking the road.

There was a black car standing sideways across the pavement. Some people were trying to push it off the road, but it wouldn't move. My mother and aunts were looking at the car, but seemed afraid to get too near. Our driver went around to the driver's door, opened it, and did something inside. The people pushed again, sending the car into a ditch. As the car rolled past me, I could see several lines of little holes up and down the doors.

"They've been machine-gunned," Fredek said. He had come up beside me. "I bet they're all dead." I hadn't looked to see if there was anyone inside, and now was glad I hadn't.

I saw Fredek try to run into the ditch after the car. But Miss Bronia was holding his hand and wouldn't let him.

"I just want to see!" he cried.

"Never mind," Miss Bronia said as she pulled him back to our truck.

CHAPTER 5

Later that morning, we stopped for a second time. That was when our driver, Mr. Dembowski, had told everyone to get under the truck, and we had been attacked by the German plane with its machine guns. Luckily, none of us was hit.

That afternoon, it grew hot in the truck. Because we couldn't drive any faster than people were walking, we got out to walk ahead of the truck. The grown-ups had decided it would also be safer because, if attacked again, it would be quicker to scramble under the truck if we didn't have to get out of the truck first.

While we were walking, we met Mr. Lupicki. He was a small man who said he had been a clerk in a shoe store. Mr. Lupicki had been walking with his suitcase, but it had been stolen when he ducked into a ditch during the strafing attack. He asked if he could ride in the truck cab with Mr. Dembowski, because he was tired and could help protect us from roaming gangs who might want to hijack the truck.

The three mothers argued over this, with my two aunts saying no and Mother saying yes. Because the truck belonged to my stepfather Lolek's factory, my mother had her way. As we walked on, Mr. Lupicki rode in the cab of the truck beside Mr. Dembowski.

As Fredek and I walked, each holding one of Miss Bronia's hands, I watched a man ahead of us helping his wife to walk. She seemed to have hurt her ankle or foot, and they were both sweating heavily with the heat. They weren't moving as fast as we were, and we soon overtook them.

Suddenly, the man's face got red, and he began to sink to the ground. Other people tried to hold him up, but he sank down out of my sight. Mr. Dembowski stopped the truck, and they put the man and his wife in the back.

We came to a grassy spot beside the road where other people had stopped to rest. When our truck pulled off the road, Mr. Dembowski stood on the running board and called out, "Is anybody a doctor?"

There wasn't a doctor, but a dentist made his way to the truck. He came out a few minutes later saying that the man had had a heart attack and died. I saw several men produce shovels and dig a grave beside the road.

That evening, when some people in a house along the way were kind enough to feed us and let us sleep on their floor, Mr. Lupicki entertained us with magic card tricks and pulled coins out of people's ears.

The next morning, Mr. Lupicki took me aside and showed me how to make a coin appear and disappear by hiding it in my palm. I would find this new skill to come in handy later.

CHAPTER 6

On the second day, I finally learned where we were going. Friends of Aunt Paula's, Mr. and Mrs. Metner, owned a farm near the town of Tarnopol, in southeastern Poland, which had once been part of a country called the Ukraine.

Mother and my aunts believed that we would be safe on the farm until the war was over. And the war would surely be over in a few weeks, as soon as Britain and France, who had an alliance with Poland, declared war on the Germans and drove them back into Germany.

Mr. and Mrs. Metner lived in Warsaw, but Mrs. Metner's mother lived in a two-story house on the farm. The peasants who worked the land for the Metners lived in cottages with roofs made of bundled hay, called *thatch*. The thatch roofs were usually bigger than the rest of the cottage and looked like giant mushrooms. One of those cottages was for visitors, and Mr. and Mrs. Metner had given us permission to stay in it until the war was over.

The cottage had walls painted white on the inside and outside. The front door opened into a large room with a huge wood-burning stove, which had to provide heat for the entire cottage in the winter.

Against one wall was a large sink made of wood and a hand pump with a curved blue handle for pumping water. There was no electricity or running water.

Mr. Dembowski and Mr. Lupicki helped us bring our belongings in from the truck. Then Mother told Mr. Dembowski that the truck was his to keep. After handshaking all around, he and Mr. Lupicki drove off. We never saw Mr. Dembowski again.

There was a bedroom for each of the mothers, and a room for Miss Bronia and Sonya to share. Fredek and I had a soft mattress on top of a cabinet in the big room.

As the mothers began unpacking and Miss Bronia

and Sonya started washing the dishes in the cottage, Fredek turned to me and said, "Let's go find us some Germans in the woods."

Knowing Fredek, this did not surprise me. "Miss Bronia is busy washing dishes," I answered.

"We don't need her," he said.

I had never gone outside without a grown-up. "What if we get lost?" I asked. I'd heard stories of children going outside by themselves and getting lost and running into witches.

"I've never been lost," Fredek said. I realized that farm children must go outside frequently without adult supervision. Some even tended sheep by themselves.

"All right," I said. "I'll just ask my mother."

"In the country, you don't need permission."

I knew that Fredek had spent summers in the country, and he must know about these things. "All right," I said, and followed him outside.

A dirt road ran in front of our cottage, with a field on the other side. "They went this way," Fredek said, turning up the rise in the road. I followed. He found a stick beside the road and began to wave it.

"Better arm yourself; they're dangerous," he advised. I picked up one and put it over my shoulder. Fredek was still waving his, and he had begun to skip. "That's no way to carry a sword," he said.

"It's not a sword. It's a rifle."

"What are you going to do with a rifle on horseback?"

"What horseback?" I asked.

"I'm on horseback. If you don't get mounted, you won't be able to keep up."

There was no refuting his logic. I began to skip as well and turned the rifle into a saber. We cantered up the hill.

Ahead of us, a large piece of farm machinery stood on the side of the road.

"A German tank," Fredek said as I pulled my mount to a stop beside his. "Here's what we do," he continued. "You pretend to surrender. Put your hands up and walk toward them slowly enough to give me time to sneak up behind them."

This was why I didn't like playing with Fredek. I was always the one to surrender or to die, while he got the glory.

"When he sticks his head and shoulders out of the turret to come out and handcuff you, I'll shoot him with my rifle."

I could have pointed out that soldiers didn't handcuff each other in battle, and that he was carrying a saber instead of a rifle, but I didn't see what that might accomplish. So I dropped my weapon, raised my hands, and began to approach, hoping there was no real person around the machine to see me. Fredek, in the meantime, crouched down and ran forward through the field.

As I got closer, I heard voices. Some men, I realized, must have been doing something on the other side of the machine. Embarrassed, I put my hands on top of my head, which, I knew, was still a legitimate surrender signal, but could also be seen as somebody just strolling along.

I saw Fredek, now standing frozen in the field beside the road. I continued walking.

I began to distinguish the men's individual words. But I couldn't understand them. They weren't speaking Polish. Fredek was moving back to me now. "Run!" he said as he passed me. "Run! They're Germans! *Real* Germans!" I wasted no time following Fredek's example.

"The Germans are here! The Germans are here!" Fredek shouted as we ran into our cottage.

Mother and Aunt Paula, who were in the big room washing clothes, stopped and looked at each other.

"Fredek?" Aunt Paula said after a moment.

"I heard them, too," I said, backing Fredek up. "They were speaking German."

"The Germans are miles away," Mother said.

"They're fighting west of Warsaw. They couldn't be here."

"Downed pilots?" Aunt Paula said.

"German spies," Fredek suggested.

"German spies?" It was Aunt Edna, now standing in the doorway to the bedrooms. "Somebody saw German spies? Where?"

I could hear the fear in her voice. "We didn't actually see them—we only heard them," I said in an effort to soften the bad news.

"There's a big farm machine up the road," Fredek said. "They were hiding behind it."

"Yulian, were they hiding?" Aunt Paula asked me.

"I guess not. They weren't whispering or anything. They were just talking. But it wasn't Polish."

"But they were speaking German," Fredek said. His tone was defensive now.

"How do you know it was German?" Mother asked. Neither of us had an answer.

"They were speaking Ukrainian," Aunt Edna said, relaxing a bit.

"Of course," Mother said.

"What's Ukrainian?" Fredek asked. I knew that the Ukraine was a country that had been divided up between Poland and Russia after the previous war, and that Ukrainians spoke a language a little like Polish.

Suddenly, Aunt Edna grew angry. "Don't either of you ever, ever frighten us like that again!" she scolded. I thought she was being unfair. We had made an honest mistake.

CHAPTER 7

Like most Polish homes, our cottage had an icebox. It was a thick-walled cabinet kept cold by a large cake of ice in its upper compartment. The melted ice was directed to a lower tray that had to be emptied every twelve hours. Emptying this tray and bringing in a fresh cake of ice every other day in a wheelbarrow was the task that was now assigned to Fredek and me.

I was thrilled. I had never had a job before. Our first effort at emptying the water was a disaster, because the shallow pan proved too tippy for our four eager hands to manage. After considerable discussion, Fredek and I decided to take turns.

Miss Bronia did all the cooking, with Sonya helping her. Every morning, they went up to the Big House, where Mrs. Metner's mother lived, and bought fresh milk and eggs from the cook. They purchased bread and vegetables from the peasants. The mothers took turns hitching wagon rides into Tarnopol to buy a newspaper and other supplies.

One afternoon, Aunt Edna came back from town with wonderful news. People were dancing in the streets, she reported, because the Russians were coming to our aid. The Russian army had crossed our eastern frontier, and Poles along the way were throwing flowers at them. The Russians would be here soon to help stop the Germans before they reached us.

The next day, Aunt Paula rode the wagon into town to find out more about how soon the Russians might be expected to make us safe. Fredek and I were pretending to be Russian soldiers that day, roaming the fields, looking for German deserters to take to our prison camp behind the house, currently occupied by our chickens. Playing our game, we were surprised by two "elephants" driving a wagon pulled by an elderly horse. The "elephants" were two young people singing in Ukrainian. Their voices were muffled through their "trunks," which had once been gas masks, whose disconnected tubes now hung loose in front.

The wagon stopped in front of us, and the elephants invited us on board. Before I knew it, Fredek and I were seated on top of the cabbages behind the elephants, who now sang in Polish. The song praised the strength of Marynka, their horse. Fredek and I joined in the song.

The kids in the gas masks seemed to be only a few years older than us, and the one driving had braids down her back. For the first time in my life, I really felt like the soldier I was playing. Now I was a Polish soldier, riding a wagon through the fields, singing with my comrades at arms.

We rode past several cottages. People outside waved to us. "Hey, Marynka!" they called to our horse. We waved back. After a while, we pulled up in front of a barn and stopped. Our two companions jumped down and removed their gas masks, transforming themselves into a boy and a girl, and began unfastening Marynka's harness.

"Can I walk her into the barn?" Fredek asked. The girl had knotted the reins over the horse's back and directed Marynka's head toward Fredek. He took hold of the reins without hesitation and led her into the barn, and the girl followed.

"Do you want to feed her?" the boy asked. I nodded.

Inside, I was struck by the smell of the place. Horse manure and hay were smells you encountered on any street in Poland, but here they were an intense mixture.

A brown kitten trotted up to us and rubbed its side against the boy's ankle. The boy reached down and petted it.

"You can pick her up and hold her," the boy said. I had never picked up any animal before, and I knelt down and held the kitten to my chest. After a moment, I could feel her purring.

Past the stalls, the boy began to climb a ladder that went straight up the wall into the loft above. I followed. I had never been allowed to climb a ladder before, but we were in the country now. Up in the loft, I could see a mountain of hay.

The boy took a pitchfork and walked over to the hay mountain. He picked up a forkful and dropped it down a hole in the floor. "That's Marynka's stall down there," he explained. Looking down the hole, I could see the top of Marynka's head as she began munching her reward.

Then he handed me the fork. "Give her two more forkfuls," he instructed. I took the fork and succeeded in wrestling four semi-forkfuls down the hole.

The boy beckoned for me to follow him up another

ladder. We climbed up right under the roof and then onto a large wooden beam over the mountain of hay. The timber was more than a foot wide, and I felt perfectly safe on it, but knew that this was not an adventure I should be sharing with Mother in any detail.

Suddenly, I felt something brush across my foot. Looking down, I saw a brown mouse scurrying away. "The cats can't get up here," the boy explained. I was glad for the mouse.

Then the boy was gone from the beam. I looked down in alarm. There he was, on his back, lying in the pile of hay. "Jump down!" he called merrily.

I understood that jumping couldn't be that dangerous, but I would have preferred to climb back down the ladder and pet the kitten. Then I saw the girl climbing up the ladder to our beam, with Fredek behind her. I jumped.

Sinking into the deep hay was softer than jumping into water or onto a mattress. But the free fall itself was the most astonishing feeling I had ever experienced. For that split moment, all my anxieties had dissolved.

In a moment, the other two kids had joined us in the hay. The boy was already climbing back up the ladder, and I ran after him.

"My airplane's on fire, and I have to bail out!" he

said before jumping. I followed right behind him, spreading my arms like an airplane. As I fell into weightlessness, a cry of joy escaped my mouth. The boy and the girl laughed. Fredek made the sound of a gun firing, staggered, and fell backward off the beam, clutching his chest.

We had done several repetitions of this delicious jump when I was suddenly gripped by fear. We must be long overdue for lunch back at the cottage. But I had no idea how to politely tell our hosts that we had to leave.

I whispered to Fredek that we had to go home. Fredek thought about this for a moment.

"We have to go home," he announced.

Without objection, our host and hostess led the way back downstairs. "You can come back tomorrow if you want to," the girl told us.

They walked us out of the barn. "Your cottage is over there," the boy said, pointing in the direction of some thatched roofs. "Follow this road until you can make a right turn."

"Good-bye and thank you," I said, as I had been taught to do. It felt so grown up. We began running down the road.

CHAPTER 8

As we neared the cottage, we could see Aunt Paula standing outside the door and shading her eyes. When she saw us across the field, she waved for us to hurry inside.

Coming through the door, we saw the three mothers sitting around the table. Neither Miss Bronia nor Sonya was there.

"Who's going to tell them?" my mother asked.

"I will," Aunt Paula said. "Frederick, Yulian, this morning I heard in town that the Russians aren't coming to fight the Germans, as we all thought. The

Russians are coming to occupy this part of Poland."

"There will be Russian soldiers with guns telling people what to do," explained Aunt Edna in a weak voice, and I saw that she had been crying. "And we will all have to do whatever they tell us."

"Or they'll shoot us," Fredek said.

The three mothers looked at one another. "Well, they could arrest us," Aunt Paula said. But I guessed that Fredek was right also.

"I won't let them shoot us," Fredek said. "I'll kick them in the shins, and I'll hit them in the head."

"My little patriot," Aunt Edna said, smiling through her tears.

"No, we're not going to do that," Aunt Paula said sternly. "We have to get through this as safely as we can until the French and the English come."

"Boys, the Russians, who now call themselves Soviets, are Communists," Aunt Paula explained. "That means they have no rich people or poor people. Everybody is the same. Nobody owns land or houses. Everything belongs to the Soviet Union. The factories all belong to the Soviet Union, too, and the people just work in them."

"So we can't let them know we have money or jewelry," Aunt Edna said, "or they'll make us share it with all the peasants."

"And if we give away our money and jewelry," my mother added, "we won't be able to buy food or clothes. The peasants know how to grow crops on the land, but we don't. So what we're going to do is hide all our jewelry and money and say we don't have any. Do you both understand?"

Fredek and I nodded.

"We've decided to sew it into our clothing," Aunt Paula said, "and pretend that we're just simple peasants. But that's all a big secret. Do you understand?"

Fredek and I both nodded again.

"We won't tell anyone where we came from or anything," my mother said. "Do you understand?"

Again we both nodded.

"And you're not to walk around the farm anymore," Aunt Edna said.

"That's right," Aunt Paula said. "Miss Bronia and Sonya are out looking for you right now. You'll have to play just in front of the cottage where we can see you."

The mothers spent the rest of the day cutting collars off their dresses and letting down hems to look more like country people's dresses.

CHAPTER 9

The next morning, Miss Bronia went up to the Big House for milk. When she returned to our cottage, she told us that she had found Mrs. Metner's mother in her kitchen, holding up her hands, surrounded by armed peasants with red armbands. These were not local peasants; they were from another town and were collecting money and valuables for "redistribution."

When the peasants asked Miss Bronia for her money and jewels, she explained that she had none, because she worked for a woman with a sick child in a cottage nearby. "Then you're a worker like us," they told her. They gave her a red armband and sent her back with a container of milk for the "sick child."

The mothers spent that morning prying their valuable gems out of their settings. They sewed the gems inside layers of cloth and disguised them as buttons for our jackets. When they finished in the early afternoon, we settled down to wait for our expected visitors.

No peasants visited us that day. But in the evening, men in blue uniforms came to our door. They were Polish border police, escaping from the Russians. They had a car full of guns and ammunition, which they spent several hours burying around our cottage. To help the men, the mothers set to work removing the insignia from their uniforms and replacing their metal buttons with buttons that had just been taken off our own clothes that morning. The men spent the night in our loft and drove away before I was awake.

We saw our first Russian soldier that day. He galloped past our house on a horse. A rifle was strapped to the back of his saddle.

As we ate supper that evening, our front door burst open, and five men and one woman strode into our big room. The men had rifles, and the woman had a pistol strapped around her middle. They all wore red armbands and helmets over their cloth caps. One, I noticed, had trouble seeing out from under his helmet.

"We are the Village Census Committee," one of the men said in heavily accented Polish. "How many people live here, and what are they called?" Aunt Paula gave him all of our names, which one of the peasants wrote down on a folded newspaper. He and another man seemed to be consulting on the spelling of our names, though they didn't ask us.

"How much money do you have?" the woman asked. Aunt Paula said we had only enough to buy food. The notetaker wrote this down as well.

There was more consultation among them, and the man who had spoken first said, "You are rich Jewish women from Warsaw. Your husbands own factories. Where is your money?"

"Our money was all in the bank," Aunt Paula said. "When the Germans started to bomb Warsaw, the banks closed, and we couldn't get our money out." This was written down as well.

The man who had trouble seeing from under his helmet kept pushing it up with his finger, but it kept coming down. I saw him pick up a candle off a table and slip it into his pocket. I looked over at Fredek. With one eye closed, Fredek was taking aim with his index finger at each of our visitors in turn.

"And your jewelry?" the spokesman asked. I noticed

that he had a sword in its decorated scabbard strapped to his side. In the Polish army, only the officers wore swords.

Aunt Edna held up her two hands, bare now of all but her wedding band. "Our jewelry is all in the bank, too," she said.

There was more consultation while Aunt Edna's answer was recorded. I saw the man who had taken the candle edging toward Sonya's orange pincushion in the shape of a mouse.

"We must search the house," the leader said a moment later. "We are under orders. Your belongings will be respected." By this time Sonya's mouse pincushion had vanished.

We stayed at the table as our visitors scattered through the cottage.

Within a few minutes, the search concluded, and the visitors reassembled in our room. "You have passed the census inspection," the man with the sword declared. "We will be in contact." Then he aimed his index finger at Fredek, fired an imaginary shot, and they were gone.

"They took my pincushion," Sonya said.

"I know, dear," her mother said. "You'll get another one."

"No, that's not what I'm saying. I was just surprised.

It isn't worth anything."

"Well, they're just Ukrainian peasants who don't like Poles, and they're taking advantage of the situation."

That night we heard several gunshots. When I woke up the next morning, the committee members were back in our house.

"Get dressed quickly," Miss Bronia anxiously told Fredek and me.

"Please, can we give the children their breakfast first?" Aunt Paula was asking the man who seemed to be in charge. "You will pack and go immediately," he commanded.

"But the children," Aunt Edna said.

"We will be back in an hour," he said. He pulled up his sleeve to look at his watch. He was wearing at least three. "Then you will get in the wagon and go to Tarnopol." He left the cottage, and the others followed.

CHAPTER 10

An old peasant with a long beard drove us into Tarnopol. We found Soviet soldiers on the street corners. Loudspeakers that had been rigged from lampposts were announcing what a wonderful place the Soviet Union was. Most of the stores we passed were closed. Where a store was open, a long line of people was waiting to get in.

The hotels were filled with Soviet army officers, and we finally found a two-room apartment in a building's ground floor. The apartment was damp and cold. It had a small stove for heating and cooking, but no firewood. The only piece of furniture was a chair, which Miss Bronia broke up for firewood to cook our supper.

That first supper in Tarnopol was carrot soup. A bunch of carrots was the only food we had been able to find for sale that first day, and they tasted awful. But we were hungry.

For our first night, we laid our clothes on the floor to make one big bed and slept without undressing. The next morning we went out in different directions to look for stores that had food for sale and for more firewood.

Walking with my mother, we came across a long line of people outside a butcher shop. Instead of going to the end of the line, as we were supposed to, Mother walked up to a man near the front of the line, who was dressed as though he was from one of the big cities. She began a conversation with him, pretending that she had mistaken him for someone she knew. When it was his turn to enter the store, the man pulled us into the store with him, to loud protests from the others on line.

I was embarrassed when we came out with a little package of lamb, and everyone on line started calling us names. But now we had something for Miss Bronia to cook. Meanwhile, Miss Bronia had found a little firewood, and Aunt Paula got some vegetables. Our dinner the second night was a lot better than the first.

A month after the start of the war, we learned that the Germans had occupied Warsaw. The fighting had been fierce, but the Germans had been preparing for war for several years, and our forces had no chance against them. Now Poland was divided between the German-occupied half on the west and the Soviet-occupied half in the east, where we were.

As the days began to get cooler, the need for firewood in our apartment became more important. Walking the streets, looking for a butcher shop selling meat or a bakery with bread to sell, we sometimes came across a wagon in the street, and a peasant man or woman selling firewood from it. We bought all that we could carry. By the time we rushed home and came back for more wood, it was all sold and the wagon was gone. Some nights we had no wood for our stove.

One day, we heard there was a train full of firewood at the train station, and you could take all you could carry. It was raining that day, and all seven of us trooped to the station in our raincoats, carrying bags to bring home the wood. A long line of people waited their turn by the single train car from which

Russian soldiers were throwing wood to the ground. Two Russian officers stood by, allowing only a few people at a time to gather wood.

My aunts and cousins all went to the end of the long line to wait their turn. Mother marched right up to the officer in charge, spoke to him in Russian, which she had learned from my Russian grandmother, and told him that I was sickly and couldn't stand in the rain with the others. Because Russian is similar to Polish, I could understand most of what she was saying. She also smiled at him and asked what part of the Soviet Union he came from.

The officer smiled back, showed Mother a photograph of his dog, and immediately detailed three soldiers to gather up firewood and follow us home with it. When the rest of our group returned hours later, soaked to the skin, Mother and I were sitting beside a nice warm stove.

The next day, Fredek had a sore throat, and the day after that, a fever. The pharmacies were all closed, and there was no way to buy medicine, not even aspirin.

Mother went to see the commissar, the town's occupation commander, a man named Colonel Wabachov, to ask for medicine for Fredek. Because she could still make herself beautiful when she wanted to, spoke Russian, and asked him questions about his own family back in Russia, the colonel took a liking to Mother and gave her a box of aspirin for Fredek, as well as a package of cheese to take home. "If there is anything else you need, come and see me," he told her.

"Yes, there is something else we need," she said. "Two days ago we had to stand in the rain at the train station to get a little firewood. It will keep our apartment warm for a week or two, but who knows when there will be more."

"I will do what I can," Colonel Wabachov answered.

The next day an ambulance arrived at our door. "My God!" Aunt Edna cried. "Your friend wants to take Fredek to the Soviet hospital. I will never see him again!"

But when the ambulance doors opened, we saw that it was filled with bags of coal for our stove.

Fredek recovered, and my two aunts were grateful. "Your friend, the commissar, is a kind man," Aunt Edna said to Mother as we sat to a dinner of soup from a chicken Miss Bronia had bought from a woman in the street. "You must go back and ask him for some meat."

"I went and begged him for aspirin because Fredek was sick," Mother answered. "I'm not going begging again."

"So what do you propose we do?" Aunt Paula asked.

"I propose we escape," Mother said.

"Escape to where?" Aunt Paula said.

"Hungary is just across the border, to the south," Mother said.

"That's Czechoslovakia," Aunt Paula corrected her. "And Hitler took it over last year."

"That's true," Mother agreed, "but there's an area that Hungary has always claimed as theirs, and Hitler gave it to them. And it's right in the Carpathian Mountains."

"And how do you expect to get there?" Aunt Edna asked. "You can't even get on a train or a bus without a travel permit. Are you going to ask your friend the colonel for a travel permit to Hungary?"

"I'll find a way," Mother said.

I could tell that my aunts didn't believe her. But I was beginning to get the feeling that when my mother set out to do something, she usually managed to get it done.

CHAPTER 11

The three mothers went out every morning, scattering in different directions, to find stores with food to sell. Fredek, Sonya, and I usually stayed home helping Miss Bronia. We had not brought warm clothes with us, and our mothers did not want us going out in the cold and getting sick, as Fredek had.

Somehow Miss Bronia had found material to sew into pallets, which we filled with straw as beds for everyone. Luckily, straw was not hard to find. Miss Bronia also found some disinfectant with which we washed the moldy walls.

One evening, Mother came home excited. "All right," she said, "I know how we're going to escape."

Aunt Edna and Aunt Paula did not seem to share Mother's excitement.

"In Lwów [*Lvoof*], which is just a short bus ride away," Mother went on, "there are local mountaineers you can hire to take you over the mountains into Hungary."

"The Carpathian Mountains?" Aunt Paula said.

"On foot?" Aunt Edna asked.

"Yes, the Carpathian Mountains and on foot. Many have already done it. You hire a local mountaineer to guide you across."

"Four women with children climbing up the Carpathian Mountains in the snow," Aunt Paula said.

"You're crazy, Barbara," Aunt Edna said.

"If the border guards don't shoot us and the wolves don't eat us, we'll freeze to death," Aunt Paula said.

"No, we won't freeze to death, because we'll be dressed warmly and we'll keep walking," Mother said. "The wolves won't eat us, because the shepherds have shot all of them. And the border guards will never suspect four women with children to be so foolish as to try to escape in the snow."

"You're crazy, Barbara," Aunt Edna repeated.

"Besides, how are you going to get to Lwów?"

Aunt Paula asked. "You need a travel permit to get on a train."

"That's the beauty of it," Mother said. "Guess who drives the bus to Lwów."

"Who?"

"Herman Lupicki."

"Who is Herman Lupicki?" Aunt Edna asked.

"He's the man we picked up on our way out of Warsaw," Mother said.

"The funny little man who pulls coins out of your ear?" Aunt Edna asked.

"Yes," Mother said. "I saw him today, and he says they only check for permits where you board the bus. But if we wait for the bus at a certain crossroads along his route, he will pick us up, and no one will ask for travel permits."

"I never trusted him," Aunt Edna said. "I didn't like his eyes."

Mother had a determined expression.

CHAPTER 12

Saying good-bye to Miss Bronia a few days later was almost as painful as Kiki's departure had been. Mother made me kiss Aunt Edna and Aunt Paula; Sonya bent over and kissed me on the forehead; and Fredek and I shook hands like grown-ups. As we drove away in the wagon Mother had hired to take us to Mr. Lupicki's pick-up location, I consoled myself with the belief that someday I would be seeing both Miss Bronia and Kiki in heaven.

Mr. Lupicki was wearing a long fur coat when he stepped off the bus to greet us. When we got on the bus, Mr. Lupicki spread a fur robe over our knees because there was no heater, and the cold wind blew in as he drove.

In Lwów, things were better than in Tarnopol. There was more food, and you didn't go hungry, although meat and eggs weren't often available. There was usually coffee and sometimes cream or sugar, but they were never available at the same time.

We rented a room in the apartment of a couple whose husband was a judge. The Soviets had closed the courts, and he was out of work. Mother found some of her Warsaw friends in Lwów and spent a great deal of time talking to people and trying to convince a guide to take us over the mountains now, in the winter snow.

Mother woke me in the middle of the night. She had no makeup on. I had never seen her face so bare before. I could hardly see her eyebrows, and her lips were the same plain color as Kiki's. Over her head, Mother had a kerchief like peasant women wore.

"You have to get up now, Yulian," she whispered. "But don't make a sound."

"What's happened?" I asked.

"*Ssshh*," Mother said. "We're starting our escape today."

I had known that Mother was planning an escape into Hungary, but I never thought it would really happen. Those things only happened to people in stories.

"Get washed quickly, and don't wake anybody. I have some bread and honey for when you get back."

Mother was wearing the dress that had diamonds wrapped in cloth for buttons, with a long black skirt over that. She saw me looking. "We will disguise ourselves as peasants," she explained. "We're taking the train to a peasant village near the border. Tomorrow our guide will take us into Hungary. Now hurry."

When I came back from the bathroom, Mother had laid out both pairs of my pants and all three shirts. "I want you to put all of these on," she said. "It's going to be cold in the mountains."

As I ate my breakfast, she said, "We're going on a great adventure, Yulian. It's going to be dangerous and difficult, but I know you're brave, and we will take care of each other. You and I are partners from now on. In a few days, we will be in a warm hotel in Budapest, where you can order anything you want to eat. And someday, when you have children and grandchildren, you will have a wonderful adventure story to tell them."

Suddenly, I realized that I had never felt as loving toward Mother as I did then.

But I didn't see any packed luggage. "Aren't we bringing suitcases?" I asked.

Mother laughed and pointed to my knapsack and a burlap bag lying beside it. "Those are our suitcases," she said. She held out two funny-looking overcoats for us to wear. Mine was her mink jacket, turned inside out, and hers was another fur coat turned inside out as well. Soon we were hurrying through the dark, empty streets toward the train station. A while after that, just as it was beginning to get light, we were sitting in a train compartment, wondering when the train would start, and hoping that the real peasant sitting across from us wouldn't see through our disguise.

Mother had warned me not to let anyone hear me speak, because we didn't speak Polish the way peasants did. I understood that, but I also believed I could speak more like a peasant than Mother could.

She had a rosary wrapped around her hand, so people wouldn't know we were Jewish. We had heard about the terrible things the Nazis had been doing to Jews in Germany since Hitler had come to power—the burning of synagogues, the smashing of Jewish stores, the imprisonment and murder of Jewish people. There were rumors that the same things were happening now in the western part of Poland, and we didn't know what the Russians might have in mind.

But Mother wasn't holding her rosary the way that Catholics held theirs. I wanted to tell Mother that, but I didn't dare speak in front of the real peasant.

I noticed that Mother kept looking out to the platform as though she were expecting someone.

As the train finally began to move, a man opened our compartment door and slipped inside.

CHAPTER 13

"Max, I was afraid you weren't coming," Mother said. She had forgotten to speak with her fake accent, but the peasant sitting across from us was asleep.

"They directed me to the wrong train," the newcomer said, out of breath. He had on a fur hat, a peasant's sheepskin jacket, and boots. When he opened his jacket, I saw a white dress shirt without its detachable collar. He wasn't a convincing peasant, either. "They've sent anyone who knows anything about running trains to Siberia, and nobody who's left here knows anything," he continued.

"Max, this is my very big son, Yulian," Mother said. "Yulian, Mr. Koppleman was a friend of your father's."

I stood up and held out my hand, the way Kiki had taught me. Mr. Koppleman, however, had taken off his fur hat and was busy combing his hair. I didn't feel right about him.

The peasant in our compartment got off at the first stop. A man in a long coat and derby hat tried to take his seat, but Mr. Koppleman yelled, "You can't come in. The child is contagious!" The man backed away.

"Are you sure this Yanek can be trusted?" Mr. Koppleman asked when we were under way again.

"How can you know about anyone these days?" Mother said. "He's taken other parties, and they've sent coded messages back to Lwów from Budapest."

I gathered that Yanek was to be our guide.

"And he's going to tell the guards that you're going to his village to marry someone?" Mr. Koppleman asked.

"That I'm going to marry *him*," Mother said, laughing.

Mr. Koppleman didn't find this funny.

"That we're going to get married in his church, and that you're my brother."

"Are you sure they'll believe him?"

"How can I be sure? But why shouldn't they believe me? Look, Max, the plan is that Yanek picks up Yulian and me in his sleigh, with his nephew driving. Then we pick you up and go straight to the mountains. When we reach the first mountain, there's a guard's shack with an officer in charge, and that's when he tells them about getting married.

"The guards know Yanek by sight. They know he goes back and forth, and they're certainly not going to think we're going to get out of the sleigh and go climbing the mountain with Yulian in all this snow.

"That road runs along the foot of the mountain. The border is along the mountain ridge. Everything on the other side is Hungary and freedom.

"There will be soldiers on foot, patrolling the road to make sure no one gets any ideas. But the men are spaced about four hundred yards apart. When the guard in front of us and the one in back are both facing away, the nephew will stop the sleigh, we jump out, Yanek puts Yulian on his back, and we all climb the mountain, while his nephew drives the sleigh on to the village. Once we reach the top, we're safe. Then we follow a stream down to a Hungarian village, where there's a train station and trains to Budapest."

Mr. Koppleman did not seem satisfied by this plan.

"What about this rabbi?" he asked after a while. "Can he be trusted?"

"Max, the rabbi and his wife have put up other escapees for the night in their house. If they get caught, they'll probably be shot."

I thought I knew what a rabbi was. He was a Jewish priest, and I had visions of him coming to the door in a long black cassock, a backward collar around his neck, and a Star of David on the end of his rosary.

Now it was dark, and Mother, Mr. Koppleman, and I were standing on the train platform. A blanket of snow covered everything. We were the only people who had gotten off the train, and our footprints were the only ones we could see. In the distance, I saw the silhouette of mountains.

"Where is everybody?" Mother asked.

"They're sitting home by the fire," Mr. Koppleman responded sourly. His answer did nothing to quell our anxiety. I gripped Mother's hand.

"Let's go; I'm freezing," Mother said.

"You said the first cottage with a green door?" Mr. Koppleman said as we stepped into the street.

"That's what Yanek told me. There will be a mezuzah on the door."

I didn't know what a mezuzah was.

"When we go inside, Yulian," Mother said, "don't take off your hat."

"Not take off my hat?" Then I remembered. Devout Jewish men didn't remove their hats in the home. Kiki had told me that. Now I remembered walking down a snowy Warsaw street in the evening, holding Kiki's hand, and I missed her all over again.

We came to the cottage with the green door. There was a little brass object on the doorframe. I couldn't see what it was, but I guessed it was the mezuzah. Mother knocked. I wondered if the rabbi would open it in his cassock and turned-around collar. How would his wife be dressed? In a nun's black habit?

The door was finally opened by a round-faced peasant woman in kerchief and apron, as I had seen many times before. "Come in quickly," she said in her peasant-accented Polish. She held a candle in a metal candleholder with a polished reflector.

Mother pushed me inside ahead of her.

"I will see you in the morning," Mr. Koppleman said, but the door was closed before he could finish. Automatically, I began to take my hat off, but stopped myself.

"Put your hat back on," Mother whispered.

A shrill voice said something I couldn't understand

from behind the peasant woman. She stepped to the side quickly, giving us a view of a tiny woman, wrapped in a gray shawl, making her slow way toward us with the help of a stick in her hand.

"I'm sorry, Rebbetzin," Mother said. "We don't speak Yiddish."

"You are crazy!" the woman said in a Jewish accent, which I had heard in Warsaw. "You are crazy in the snow with the child!"

The woman shuffled across the floor. Behind her, someone was coughing.

"I know you think this is foolish," Mother answered. "But the authorities aren't watching the border as much as they will in warm weather. I have a young son, and I don't want him growing up a Bolshevik."

The woman stopped directly in front of us, holding eyeglasses on a silver stick up to her eyes. By the candlelight, the white skin on her hands and face looked almost transparent. In place of the white hair I would have expected, she had a full head of orange-colored waves and curls. It had to be a wig. Although she stood perfectly straight, she was no taller than I was. She examined us both through her handheld glasses. The peasant woman brought the candle a little closer to our faces.

"Why you don't speak Yiddish?" the old woman asked.

"I'm sorry, Rebbetzin," Mother said. "My mother is Russian, and we spoke Russian and Polish at home, not Yiddish."

The woman made a sound that showed her displeasure. "Go eat," she said, waving her stick toward the back of the room. Following the stick with my eyes, I could see a table near a stove, dimly lit by a lamp.

Two wooden armchairs stood at right angles to each other near the light, and for the first time, I noticed a bundled figure in one of the chairs. It was a man with a long white beard, and he was wearing a black coat, a wide-brimmed hat, and gloves with the fingertips cut off. His glasses were perched halfway down his nose. I saw him lick his fingertips before turning a page in the book he was reading. He seemed unaware of our presence.

The old woman indicated that we should sit at the table.

"Take off your coat," Mother said to me, "but keep your hat on." A strong meat and vegetable smell came from the stove, and I realized I was hungry.

We sat down across from each other, and the younger woman brought us bowls of steaming stew and wooden spoons. This was accompanied by a thick slice of unbuttered black bread for each of us.

"Blow, it's hot," Mother said to me. The pieces of meat and vegetables had a strong smell. I blew on a spoonful and sipped the stew carefully. I didn't like the taste.

"It's delicious," Mother said over her shoulder. "What is it?"

The old woman said something I could not understand.

"Goat," the round-faced woman translated.

I actually heard myself gulp. There had been goats on the farm—smelly, aggressive animals that ate garbage and had horns like Satan. That strong flavor now curdled on my tongue, and I began to gag.

Mother looked at me, and I fought to control my gag. All I needed now was to throw up on this woman's table.

"Eat," the old woman encouraged.

"Try it, Yulian. It's good," Mother urged quietly. There was no way I could swallow this, even if I wanted to.

"You have to eat," Mother said more firmly. "We have a long trip tomorrow."

I shook my head.

"Eat just the vegetables and the bread," Mother said.

I shook my head again. I tried eating the coarse bread, but without butter, it wouldn't go down my throat, either.

"You can't have butter now," Mother whispered. Then she turned to the two women. "He can't eat the stew. Is there something you can put on his bread?" she asked. The women exchanged some words in Yiddish.

I heard some shuffling behind me. In a moment the younger woman had placed another slice of black bread in front of me, this one covered with a white, jellylike substance.

I bit into it hungrily. It was greasy and like nothing I had tasted before.

The old woman must have noticed my reaction. "Schmaltz," she said.

"It's goose lard, and it's delicious," Mother said.

I put the bread down and shook my head.

"You have to eat something," Mother said. The taste of grease was still in my mouth, and I shook my head again. From the man in the chair came a series of dry coughs.

"He isn't used to this kind of food," Mother explained to the women. "He needs to eat something— we have a hard journey tomorrow. Can you give him some butter or cheese? He hasn't touched the meat." I really did not understand what the fuss was about.

The old woman exchanged some words with the

man, and he coughed some more. Then she spoke to the younger one. The peasant woman busied herself at the cupboard and returned with another slice of bread. On top of the bread was a thick slice of white cheese. In her other hand she carried a cup. But instead of setting them down, she indicated with her head that I was to follow her. Mother nodded her consent.

The cheese beckoned, and I followed.

The woman led me to the empty chair next to the old man and indicated that I should sit. I had the feeling that I was trespassing in a private space. The old man coughed again and went on with his reading, ignoring me.

I sat down, pretending not to look at him, while the woman handed me the plate and the cup.

Resting the cup on the arm of the chair and the plate in my lap, I cautiously bit into the cheese. It had a tangy flavor that I liked. The milk in the cup was thicker than what I knew and had a taste similar to the cheese. I ate eagerly.

I lowered my face so I could secretly observe the old man. I saw his legs and feet bundled in a blanket, despite the heat from the stove. I wondered if he could walk. I watched him moisten his fingertips to turn a page. He seemed to be muttering to himself.

I presumed this was the rabbi, and that he had

grown too old to conduct services. I wondered how he felt about his approaching death without the possibility of entering heaven, because he wasn't Catholic. I wondered if he knew about heaven. Here, I realized, was an old man who knew that he would soon be dying. It might happen next month or next week, or even tonight. But he was just calmly sitting there waiting for it to happen.

He was even reading. Reading to learn new things, even though tomorrow his brain might no longer know anything. I recalled how I had felt when Kiki and I built sand castles on the beach that I knew soon would be washed away. I didn't feel bad for myself, because I could always build another sand castle. I felt bad for the castle, which didn't even know that its existence would be ended by the next tide.

But here was a man who knew his fate and just sat there reading. It was so sad—sad and gripping. I could not take my eyes from the poor, doomed man.

Then he caught me staring at him. I looked away instinctively. I diverted my eyes to my lap and the floor, until the younger woman finally took Mother and me to where we would be sleeping that night.

Three walls of our room were stone, and the one window was a narrow slit just below the ceiling. I guessed we were below ground level. A kerosene lamp glowed on the table. It was cold in the room. "We'll keep our clothes on tonight," Mother said. I had no problem with that.

"Come here and sit down with me," Mother said, sitting down on the bed. The mattress did not seem to give under her. "I want to tell you something." I sat down beside her on the bed. "I told you, Yulian, that this is the home of a rabbi," Mother began. "These people are pious Jews. Do you know what that means?"

"That they pray a lot," I speculated.

"That's right, they pray a lot. And they closely obey the laws God gave them."

Now this was interesting. "What kind of laws did God give to Jews?" I asked.

"Well, one law is not to eat meat and milk or things made from milk, like butter, at the same time. That's why you couldn't have butter on your bread while the stew was on the table."

This seemed like a strange issue for God to concern Himself with. "What other laws are there?" I asked.

"Well, I'm not sure what the exact law is, but Jewish men and boys have to keep something on their heads all the time and never cut the hair in front of their ears."

I was glad my parents weren't pious Jews, but I didn't say it. Instead, I said, "That's different from the laws that God gave Catholics."

"Oh, what laws are those?"

"Well, they have laws about being good. One is not to kill people and another is not to steal anything."

My mother surprised me by laughing at this. "Those are the Ten Commandments."

"Yes, that's what they're called, about lying and going to church on Sundays."

"Yulian, God gave the Ten Commandments to the Jews. Don't you know that?"

Now I was confused. "Then how did Catholics get them?" Kiki had shown me a gray card with the Ten Commandments printed on it.

"My poor Yulechek." Mother laughed. "What has Miss Kiki been teaching you? Don't you know that the first Christians were Jews?"

Mother was talking nonsense now. How could Christians be Jews?

"Jesus," Mother went on, "was a Jew."

This was outrageous! "What do you know about Jesus?" I demanded.

"A few things."

I knew I shouldn't allow Mother to say things like that about Jesus. "All right, where was He born?"

"In Bethlehem," she answered. "His mother's name was Mary, and his father was a carpenter named Joseph."

She was right. She did know about Jesus.

"Bethlehem was in Judea, which is Palestine now," she continued. "That's where Jews used to live."

I knew that my grandfather on my father's side lived in Palestine now. "Well, if Jesus was a Jew," I asked, knowing that I had her now, "how come He's in heaven?"

"Because God loves Him," Mother said.

"God loves Jews?"

My mother closed her eyes and leaned her head back against the wall behind her. "God loves everyone," she said. "Didn't Miss Kiki teach you that? He loves Jews and Catholics and Arabs—who call him Allah—and Chinese people who don't even worship Him."

"How about Negroes in Africa, and Indians in America?"

"Them, too. He even loves people who don't believe He exists."

This seemed like a God who was much easier to live with.

"So does that mean the rabbi will be going to heaven," I asked, "even though he isn't Catholic? I mean, when he dies?"

"Of course. What kind of God wouldn't let people into heaven just because they were born Jewish or Chinese? Would that be a loving God?

"Of course the rabbi is going to heaven when he dies," Mother continued. "He is a good man. If the Russians knew that he and his wife helped people like us to escape, they would be arrested. Maybe even shot. They're not only good, but brave people."

I had goose bumps. These people were real heroes, like the ones Kiki used to tell about, people who risked their lives to fight for Poland or to stand up for what was right. And here I was, right in their house.

"You're kind to be concerned about the rabbi getting into heaven," Mother said. "It means that you're a good person, too. But I've known that for a long time."

Suddenly, I was hugging my mother, joyful the rabbi was going to heaven and about what Mother had just said about me.

I could tell that it surprised her as well. As she hugged me back, I could hear little sniffs, which meant she was crying. It all felt surprisingly good. Mother, still in her kerchief, her eyes without makeup and now crying, suddenly wasn't a "grown-up" anymore, but someone who was a part of me, almost the way Kiki and I had been.

We held on to each other for a while and finally Mother pulled away gently. "It's so funny," she said with a little laugh followed by another sniff, "through all these layers of clothing. We feel so fat." I laughed, too, and it felt good to be laughing together.

"You know, when I was your age, maybe a little older," Mother said, "I used to love adventures. One time, my brother, Pawel, and I were spending the summer on a farm with Grandmother. I discovered that I could climb up high in the barn and jump down into this big stack of hay."

"Fredek and I did that on the farm, too!" I interjected.

"You did?" Mother said in surprise.

"Yes," I admitted, wondering if I hadn't angered Mother now.

"And did you have the feeling for just a second that you were flying?" she asked.

"I did," I said, nodding enthusiastically. "I spread my arms like this," I said, demonstrating, "and I felt like an airplane."

We both laughed again. Mother put her arms out like mine. Later, when Mother's face grew serious, I knew what she was going to say. "You'd better get some sleep now," she said.

I took off my shoes and lay on the bed. Mother laid my coat over me on top of the blankets.

"Don't worry about anything," she said, tucking me in. "The guards don't expect a woman and a boy to be trying to escape in this weather. They won't be suspicious of us."

I reached up, and Mother pressed her soft face against mine.

CHAPTER 14

They were whispering when I woke up in the middle of the night. The kerosene lamp was glowing dimly, and I could see Mother and Mr. Koppleman sitting at the table.

"They were dressed as women," Mr. Koppleman was saying in an agitated voice.

"Maybe they weren't convincing," Mother said, her calm voice contrasting to his. "Maybe they hadn't shaved recently—how do I know? Discover two men dressed as women in a sleigh and what else are you going to think?"

"Well, they're all going to be on the alert now," he said. Instinct told me to pretend sleep.

"They won't suspect *me* of being a man," Mother said. She sounded angry now.

"That's not going to save you when they see you jump out of the sleigh. No, Basia, it's too dangerous for us now. I'm not going."

"You're not going? Max, please. I need you to help with Yulian."

"Don't be ridiculous. I'm not going, and you're not going, either. The snow is a three feet deep, and you wouldn't make it even if you were alone."

"I don't care how deep it is. We are going. Max, please. Be a man—I need you."

"You're not going. I forbid you!"

"You forbid me? *You're* being ridiculous. You're afraid."

"Yes, I am afraid. I'm afraid for you and the boy. I was Nahtek's friend. What would he have said?" Nahtek was my birth father, Nathan.

"Nahtek is dead. If we get through this, Yulian will have today to look back on for the rest of his life and know that he did something heroic. It's the most I can give him right now."

"I *am* thinking of Yulian," Mr. Koppleman said, but with little conviction.

"You're not a man," Mother said. "Go back to Lwów. I don't want to look at you anymore!"

"Basia, you don't know what you're doing. It's suicide. I'm begging you." Now he sounded as though he really was begging.

"Get out of here!" Mother hissed. I had never heard her so angry. "I don't want to look at your face."

"You're crazy, Barbara. You're a crazy woman."

"Get out, Max," she said again, but in an even voice this time.

Mr. Koppleman turned and marched out of the room.

A few hours later, Mother woke me again. "Get washed, Yulian," she said. "Breakfast is almost ready."

I made a face, remembering how cold the water had been last night. Mother laughed. "I poured you some warm water," she said. Today would be the first time in my life I'd ride in a sleigh or climb a snow-covered mountain.

Then I remembered last night's scene with Mr. Koppleman, which Mother didn't know I had overheard. I wondered if anything had changed after I had gone back to sleep. Had Mr. Koppleman come back to say he had changed his mind and was going with us? Or had Mother changed her mind and decided not to go?

"Alicia is making scrambled eggs for you," Mother said. Scrambled eggs were my favorite food, but I was allowed them only rarely. "Yanek will be here soon," Mother said. That meant that we were still going! But the wait became longer than we expected.

"He should have been here hours ago," Mother said later that morning, speaking more to herself than to me. A little later she said angrily, "You don't keep people waiting three hours."

Finally, there was a knock on our door. Mother went to open it, and I saw a young man's face above a sheepskin jacket. He wore no hat, and his black hair fell a little over his dark eyes.

He looked around the room quickly. "Where is Koppleman?" he asked. "They said he's gone back to Lwów?"

"He has," Mother said. "He changed his mind."

"I don't give back money," the young man said. His accent was different from the peasant accent I had become accustomed to.

"He doesn't ask for his money," Mother said. "This is my son, Yulian. We're ready to go."

The young man turned and led the way out of the house. Mother stopped to put a shawl over her head, then detoured to say good-bye to the rabbi's wife. The woman and the younger one were at the table peeling vegetables. "Thank you for your hospitality," Mother said, handing something to the older woman.

The woman said something I didn't understand, and Mother bowed her head respectfully. Then Mother handed something to the younger woman, who had stood up. The woman curtsied.

"Good-bye, Rabbi," Mother said, turning toward the two armchairs, and I realized that the old man was back in his chair.

"He doesn't hear," the old woman said.

Mother crossed to where the old man was sitting. I saw him look up at her. He began to say something, but started to cough instead. Mother leaned over and patted one of his gloved hands. Then she and I followed Yanek outside.

"It's snowing!" Mother said. Large flakes were floating lazily to the ground.

"The Bolsheviks don't see so well in the snow," Yanek answered.

There stood a horse and a sleigh. The horse was brown with a black mane and tail. His muzzle was plunged into a leather feed bag. At the front of the sleigh, a boy, not much older than I, causally leaned against the reins hanging over the dashboard. A black whip stood in its holder beside him. Suddenly, I was filled with envy and would have changed places with him in an instant.

Yanek pulled back a corner of the sleigh's fur blanket and awkwardly extended a hand to help Mother climb into the sleigh. I followed.

"That's all. The other isn't coming," Yanek said to the boy. Yanek walked to the front to unstrap the feed bag from the horse. The boy made a clucking sound, and the horse stepped forward. Yanek stepped on the runner as the sleigh moved past and casually swung himself into the sleigh beside me.

Nobody said anything as the sleigh picked up speed. The little village was quickly left behind. The road of packed snow stretched ahead of us in a straight line as far as I could see.

CHAPTER 15

I had never had cold wind blow in my face that way before. I opened my mouth to catch snowflakes. Mother kept looking straight ahead toward the mountains. "So Missus lived in a big house in Warsaw?" Yanek said after a while.

"An apartment," Mother answered, not taking her eyes off the mountains.

"Missus travels much?" he asked. I had the impression that he was trying to start a conversation.

"No," Mother told him. That wasn't true, so I understood that she didn't want to talk.

Later, the man said, "When we talk to the border guards, I will have to say 'you' to Missus, like I would to my sweetheart." "You" was the less formal way to address people.

"That's all right," Mother said. "Mister can call me 'you' now if he wants."

"Maybe I will practice," he said with a laugh. "How do you like the sleigh ride?"

"I like riding in your sleigh very much." I could tell that Mother was trying to be polite, but her mind was elsewhere.

"Our village is behind that mountain," Yanek said, pointing to our left. "When we reach that little mountain over there," he went on, pointing straight ahead this time, "the road will stop, and another road will go along the foot of the mountain. First there will be a guardhouse, and that is where I will tell that Missus—I mean you—are coming to marry me in my village. Then we turn left toward my village, and there will be guards walking back and forth along the road about every four hundred yards."

I had heard all this yesterday.

"When they can't see us anymore from the guardhouse, Antek will stop and feed the horse. Then, when I see the guard in front and the guard in back both walking away from us, we will jump out of the sleigh and walk as fast as we can to the top of the mountain. I will carry Missus's son on my back. Once we are on top of the mountain, we are safe across the border. Then we walk down to the Hungarian village."

"I understand," Mother said. Nobody said anything else until we reached the guardhouse just before the mountain.

Two soldiers, in their long coats and green pointed hats, came out of the guardhouse as we approached. Antek reined the horse to a stop, and Yanek surprised me by addressing them in neither Polish nor Russian. I now recognized it as Ukrainian, which is similar to both, but not a language I understood except for the odd Polish- or Russian-sounding phrase. I made out that he was explaining that he was bringing Mother home to marry her. His tone was jolly, and the two soldiers laughed. Yanek handed one of the soldiers some folded papers, at which the man only glanced before handing them back.

The soldier now walked around to Mother's side of the sleigh and reached for her shawl. He pushed some of it back from Mother's face. Mother lowered her eyes shyly, which I knew wasn't a genuine gesture. The soldiers said something to Yanek, and they all laughed. I saw the boy, Antek, blushing.

The second soldier had lifted a corner of the fur robe to look underneath. He seemed satisfied that no one was hiding there. The guard said something else to Yanek, which I could tell by his body language meant for us to go.

At that point, Yanek produced a bottle of red wine from a pocket deep inside his jacket. He raised it over his head, then tossed it across the sleigh to one of the guards. Catching it deftly, the soldier raised it the same way over his own head. He said something to Mother, who again lowered her eyes in that pretend shy way. Then Yanek said something to Antek, who slapped the reins, and we were on our way again.

"They will drink to our health," our guide said to Mother with a wink.

Looking ahead for the first time, I saw the mountain not a hundred yards in front of us. It was a long, fairly straight ridge with trees on top, but nothing other than snow on the slope. It didn't look that high.

"That's the border, up there where the trees begin," Yanek explained.

"They cleared all the trees between here and the border. But don't worry. If we don't show ourselves to the guard, he won't see us," he said with another wink, a statement that seemed too obvious to make sense.

"We climb to the top as fast as we can, before they change the guard, then follow the stream down to the village."

I could not help looking at Yanek with admiration and looked forward to my ride up the hill on his back.

We came to the end of our road, and the horse turned left on his own. Ahead, I saw another soldier walking in the same direction as we were heading. It wasn't until our horse drew even with him that the soldier noticed our presence. Turning quickly, he seemed to recognize Yanek and grinned. Yanek shouted something to him and threw him a bottle of wine, too. The soldier fumbled as the bottle fell through his hands into the snow. He bent over to pick it up, then raised it to show he had recovered it as we moved on.

Soon we passed another soldier, who recognized Yanek as well. Yanek threw him another bottle.

"They all know Mister, don't they?" Mother said

"I make sure they like me," Yanek answered. Then Antek pulled the horse to a stop. Far ahead, I could see a speck that must have been the next border guard.

Antek got out of the sleigh with the leather feed bag, and I knew this was where we would be jumping into the snow. My heart began to race.

"Put your knapsack on your back," Mother said to me. I obeyed.

CHAPTER 16

Yanek stood up and turned to look back. Mother and I turned with him. The guard behind us raised his wine bottle as though in greeting and turned around to walk the other way.

"All right, quickly," Yanek whispered. "Jump!"

Mother scrambled out of the sled and into the snow beside the road. She sank almost to her knees. A little cloud of snow rose up around her legs.

"It's light snow," Yanek said behind me as I followed Mother.

There was something slippery under the snow,

and I found myself sitting down. The snow was up to my shoulders.

"Oh, Yulian!" Mother said. "Get up quickly." She began fumbling for my hand. "Are you all right?"

"I'm all right," I assured her. Getting to my feet with the backpack wasn't easy. Mother pulled me up. I was standing almost to my hips in snow.

"Oh my God!" Mother suddenly cried.

I turned in the direction she was looking. I saw our sleigh pulling away from us—fast. Holding the reins, slapping them sharply along the horse's back, was our guide, Yanek.

"He's left us!" Mother said. Then she called him some names I had never heard before, and I was afraid the guard would hear her. "He took my money, and then he abandoned us! He was supposed to carry you!"

Suddenly, Mother was trudging through the snow after the sleigh. I looked back at the guard, who, miraculously, hadn't heard us. I ran after Mother. The snow was surprisingly light and offered little resistance.

"It's only to the top of the hill," I said. "I can climb that by myself. Then we just follow the stream to the village."

Mother stopped and turned to face me. I could see

her forcing a smile. "My little soldier," she said.

"We have to hurry before the guard sees us," I said.

"Yes, yes," she agreed. "We can't stay here."

I started up the hill, hoping she would follow.

In a moment, Mother had passed me. "Get behind me," she commanded, "and walk in my tracks."

"No," I insisted. "I can walk by myself."

"Walk behind me," Mother repeated. "We can take turns breaking the snow."

That I could agree with. I moved into Mother's tracks, where the going was easier. But we were on the slope now, and the footing was slippery. We were making little headway.

Mother seemed to be having more trouble than I was. Instead of pushing her legs through the light snow, she kept trying to lift her feet up over it. I saw her stagger a few times as she slipped. Finally, she lost her footing altogether and sat down hard. I realized she no longer had her bag.

"Do you want me to go back get your bag?" I asked. I didn't hear an answer.

"I'll hurry," I assured her.

"I said no!" Mother shouted.

Instinctively, I looked back at the guard again. He was still walking away from us and had the wine bottle raised to his lips.

"We have to go on," Mother said, to my relief. She got to her hands and knees and began crawling up the hill on all fours.

Soon Mother was making better headway than I was, so I had little choice but to follow her example. There were tree stumps hidden under the snow, making the footing more difficult.

We kept crawling up the slope. I understood that if we reached a certain height before the guard turned around, he wouldn't be as likely to spot us.

Mother wasn't crawling as fast as I could have. I heard her labored breathing. I kept looking over my shoulder at the guard, still with his back to us.

Suddenly, my right arm sank into a deep hole, stopping only when my face pressed against the packed snow. I tried to pull out my arm, but something under the snow held it. Terror gripped me.

"What is it?" Mother asked in alarm. I realized that I had begun to cry.

"I can't get my arm out!" I said, my face buried in snow. "Something's grabbed me!"

"*Ssshh*," Mother said. "I'm coming."

"Hurry!" I was covered in sweat. "It's pulling me down."

"It's not pulling you down. Be quiet."

I clenched my teeth. Mother reached down into

the snow and pulled up on my sleeve. I felt my arm release. "There's a crust under the snow here, and your hand broke through," Mother explained. "Just put your elbows down so your weight is on your whole forearm, and come on." She turned and started up the hill again.

I looked down at the road to see if the guard had heard us. I saw him turn and begin walking back in our direction. "The soldier is walking back toward us," I said, making sure there was no alarm in my tone.

"Don't worry about him," said Mother. "Just climb."

I wondered why we shouldn't worry. Would the wine make him drunk, so he wouldn't be able to see or shoot at us? We were only about a quarter of the way up the mountain. I could see him walking his post still apparently oblivious of us.

After a while Mother stopped. "We have to . . . rest," she said, out of breath. She lay down in the snow. "Lie down. It'll . . . make it harder . . . for anyone to see us."

I lay down, though I didn't need to rest. I could feel my heart beating a little faster, but I was not out of breath like my mother.

Below us, I could see a long sleigh, like a farm wagon on runners, pulled by two horses, following the route our sleigh had traveled. It was filled with soldiers.

"Look, there are more soldiers coming," I said. "I think they're going to change the guard."

"Keep your head down," Mother ordered. "Don't move."

I didn't need to be told that. I made myself as flat as possible, the side of my face against the snow, the way Kiki's brother had done on the battlefield in the last war. I could no longer see the sleigh and hoped it meant the soldiers couldn't see us, either.

"All right, we have to be careful now. There's a new guard—don't let him see you," Mother said after some time. "We have to crawl the rest of the way on our stomachs. And don't make any noise."

I had played this in our Warsaw apartment, crawling along the floor between chair legs, the way Kiki's brother had crawled under the barbed wire. I kept the side of my face down, turned my feet out so that my heels wouldn't stick up, and followed Mother.

But she didn't seem to know about turning your feet out, and the heels of her boots bobbed up and down in front of me.

"Put your heels down," I said in a loud whisper.

"Ssshh, be quiet," Mother whispered back. She hadn't put her face down sideways, either, and I could see the top of her head in its shawl.

"Turn your toes out so your feet lie flat and put

your face down on its side," I said.

"Hush!" Mother said.

I let it go—soon we were nearing the top.

The ground wasn't as steep anymore. "Yulian," Mother said, "when I give the signal, we're going to stand up and run as fast as we can into the woods. I know how fast you can run."

This couldn't be true—Mother had never seen me run. And it was unlikely that Kiki had told her the results of the races we had had on the beach. Mother was just trying to encourage me.

For what seemed like forever, Mother lay still, breathing hard. I knew what she was doing—she was resting up for the sprint to the top.

"Now!" she whispered. Then she assumed a crouched position and began running up the hill. I followed and beat her to the top. In a moment, Mother was hugging a tree for support at the top of the hill, trying to catch her breath again.

I heard strange gasps from Mother and realized she was laughing while still gulping for air. She slid down the trunk and sat. "Yulian," she said, "we're out of Poland. Do you realize that? We've escaped the Bolsheviks!"

Mother was peering down at the new guard, the one who hadn't had any wine to drink, who now was looking up at us. He had probably noticed us when we had made that last dash. He was standing in the snow, a few feet from the road with his hands on his hips. Now that we were across the border, there was nothing he could do.

After a while, Mother stood up again. "We're not there yet. There's a long walk ahead of us," she said. "And where is that coward Max?"

I remembered the way Mother had been last night, telling me about when she had been a little girl and about God.

"He's back in a café in Lwów," she said, answering her own question. Then she began to laugh. But this time it wasn't a fun laugh. "He's sitting there telling everyone that we've either been shot or arrested. And they're all saying, 'That crazy Barbara. Serves her right.'"

The image of Mr. Koppleman sitting in a café and telling everyone that we had been either shot or arrested made me aware of the serious nature of what we were doing.

"All right," Mother said. "Now let's find that stream. We'll have some lunch there and a drink of clear mountain water."

Lunch sounded good. "How are we going to find the stream?" I asked.

"Yulian, where does water always flow?"

I couldn't tell if she was reproaching me for something I should have learned in school.

"Hmmm?" she asked. "Which direction does water always flow in? You know." By the tone of her voice, I now knew it was a friendly question. Then I realized the answer. "Downhill!" I said. "Water always flows downhill. So it must be down there somewhere, right?" I pointed down the wooded slope.

"Exactly right! Now we get to go downhill. And when we get to Budapest, we will have a hot bath, a soft bed, and anything you want to eat."

"Will we be in Budapest tonight?"

"Probably not tonight. We have to find the village first."

"Right, follow the stream to the village."

As we started into the woods, I saw that Mother was crying with relief.

CHAPTER 17

Going downhill was only a little less steep than it had been coming up, except now we had trees to hold on to. Mother walked cautiously, stopping against each tree. I found that by locking my knees I could slide down from tree to tree. At one point I missed my tree and found myself gathering speed. I passed Mother and was heading straight for a log lying across my path.

Instinctively, I sat down. I continued sliding, but at a more controlled pace. I raised both feet and was able to cushion my stop against the log.

"Good idea," Mother said behind me, holding on to a tree. She sat down, too, and, holding her skirt around her legs, soon joined me against the log. She laughed. "This is fun," she said.

It was getting late in the day. I peered into the twilight for the bottom of the hill and our stream, but could see neither. What if Yanek had lied about the stream as well?

Mother crawled over the log and sat down on the other side. "Here we go!" she said gaily. Wiggling a little in the snow, she began to lead the way again. Bumping our way from tree to tree, we continued down the hill.

I saw Mother raise her arm over her head and point to our left. There I could now see jagged sheets of ice and crusted snow that I realized must mark our stream. It ran downhill at a slant. On the other side of the stream, the ground rose again, and I had the feeling that we were sliding into a giant funnel.

Suddenly, Mother's downward progress stopped with a jolt and a cry of pain. I lay down on my side to avoid crashing into her. I began to roll, then stopped by grabbing a low-hanging tree limb.

Mother's left foot was sticking out from under the branch of a fallen tree.

"My leg is stuck under this log," she said.

I worked my way back to where she was. "Can't you pull it out?" I asked.

"No, I can't," she said angrily.

"What if I help pull?"

"No!"

"Does it hurt?"

"Yes it does. See if you can lift the log."

"Did you break your bone?"

"I don't know. Try and lift it off my leg."

I straddled the branch and reached down to lift it. It wouldn't budge.

"Maybe we can lift it together," Mother said. But I could see that she couldn't get enough of an angle to be of much help.

"What are we going to do now?" I asked.

Mother kicked at the log with her other foot. "Ow!" she cried. "Find something to pry it off," she said. "Go find a stick about this big around," Mother said, indicating a two-inch diameter with her fingers, "and as tall as you are."

I tried breaking off another branch of the same tree she was pinned under, but it wouldn't break. I looked around, but saw nothing else to match the requirements. "I don't see anything," I said.

"Walk around and look," Mother said. "There's got to be something."

Nothing like that showed above the snow, so I began to crawl on all fours to our right.

I spotted a large boulder ahead of me. Its shape and size looked like a tank pointed downhill. I thought of Fredek and our adventure with the farming machine and "German spies." But today wasn't make-believe. Mother and I had just escaped from the real Soviets, these were real woods, and Mother had her leg caught under a real log.

"Yulian, are you looking?" I heard behind me.

"Yes!" I yelled back. "But I don't see anything!"

"Try on the other side, by the stream!"

I turned around and headed back.

"Hurry," Mother said as I crossed in front of her.

I could hear the stream gurgling in front of me, though I couldn't see it. The stream was hidden below the level of the snow. There were sheets of ice, several feet across, which had been pushed up onto the bank by the current. They stuck up in the air, reminding me of an ice-cream wafer. One wafer was in the shape of a big leaf. Another was like a sailboat.

"Do you see anything?" Mother cried, ending my daydream. "Can you hear me?"

"Yes, I'm looking!" I knew I had done wrong letting my mind wander. I determined to pay attention.

Finally, there was something that might do the

trick, stuck right in the middle of the water, a few yards downstream. A thick branch was planted in the stream as if it had grown there, except with the thicker end up.

I didn't know if I could reach it. Lying flat on my stomach, I reached over the stream's bank for the branch, but I couldn't grab it.

I wiggled farther over the rushing water. I heard the crust crack under my weight and panicked as I felt myself go down. But I dropped only a little, and finally had the stick.

"Yulian!" Mother called.

"I've found something!" I yelled back

Soon I was half crawling, half running back to Mother, with the pole in my hand.

"You found one!" Mother said.

Suddenly, the sight of my mother trapped under a log was a shock. It was like seeing her vulnerable for the first time.

Feeling guilty, I jammed the thin end of the pole under the log and pushed. It broke.

"Use the other end," Mother said. I turned the branch and tried again.

"Ow!" Mother cried when I began moving the log.

"I'm sorry," I said. I really was sorry—I had caused Mother more pain.

"It's all right," Mother said calmly now. "Put the stick in a little farther and push straight up. I'll help you."

Mother put her free foot against the log. Together we pushed up on the pole, and, with another cry of pain, her leg was free.

I saw a big hole in her woolen stocking and clotted blood all over her shin. I felt a shiver, as I usually did at the sight of blood. "Is it . . . is it broken?" I asked.

"Just a minute," Mother said. She carefully turned her foot. I saw her wince and felt guilty over imagining the tank and the ice-cream wafers while she had been hurting.

"Help me stand," Mother said. I helped her to her feet. "Let me lean on you." She held my shoulder. I felt her weight shift slowly as she tested her leg.

"Is it all right?" I asked anxiously.

"Yes, I think it is. It just hurts. Let me have that stick."

I shouldered my backpack, slid down to the next tree, and stretched my hand out for her. Mother bit her lip and reached out for my hand. Leaning heavily on my hand, she carefully slid down to my tree.

I waited while she took some deep breaths. This time, instead of holding out my hand, I waited until I saw Mother begin to ease herself away from the tree.

Then I reached out my hand and caught hers. In this manner we worked our way down the hill. When we reached the bottom, my arm and shoulder ached from the effort.

There seemed to be a trail beside the stream. The snow covered any marks on the ground, but it was hard to miss the path where branches had been broken off by some sort of traffic, which was an encouraging sign.

I waited to see if Mother wanted to rest. She didn't, so I set out breaking a trail in the four or five inches of loose snow. Mother shuffled along behind with the aid of her stick.

I walked at a slow pace. Every few minutes I looked over my shoulder to make sure I wasn't going too fast. Mother's face was set in a grim expression.

"I have to stop for a minute," Mother said behind me. We were just approaching a fallen tree on which we could sit. "Yulian, go down to the stream and get some water," she said, thrusting a tin cup at me.

After bringing water back to her, I saw Mother sitting with her injured leg straight out in front of her. "Would you like some?" she asked.

I shook my head.

"Drink some," she said.

"It's all right—I'll go back for more," I assured her.

"You're hot, aren't you," she said. I hadn't been

aware that I was, but I realized she was right. "Why don't you undo your jacket," she suggested. I untied the piece of string around my waist.

"Sit down for a minute and rest," Mother said.

If she was ready to go, I was, too. "I'm not tired," I said.

"You can leave that here now," Mother said as I lifted my backpack.

"No," I said. "I want to keep it."

"All right, we should get going," Mother said, struggling to her feet. "It's beginning to get dark."

CHAPTER 18

We were on our way again, and now I had a new worry as evening approached. Wolves hunted at night in forests.

Then I remembered Mother telling me that hunters had killed all the wolves, except the ones in zoos. But what if a zoo had been bombed, and the wolves had escaped?

But I had to be a grown-up now. Mother wasn't afraid of wolves, so I had to rid myself of my childish fears. Besides, Kiki had said that if you have faith, God will protect you. Now I wondered whether that was really true, or if it was another story meant for kids.

But if you had doubts, your faith *couldn't* work, could it? What Kiki said had to be true. God would protect us because He was all-loving and all-powerful. But what about Mother's faith? I realized that my faith would have to be strong enough to protect us both. "Would you like to lean on my shoulder?" I asked.

Mother smiled for the first time. "No, thank you, Yulian. You know, my leg doesn't hurt as much anymore."

I noticed that she was walking a little more easily now, and she no longer had a grim expression. Only when I felt her squeeze back did I realize that I had taken her free hand in my own.

"What a pair of adventurers we are," Mother said. All I could do was nod, trying to not show the pleasure I was feeling. I let go of my mother's hand and resumed breaking the trail for her.

"No," Mother said, taking hold of my hand again. "I'd rather hold your hand now."

We began walking side by side. It was getting darker. The trees around us no longer had definition but were simply black lines across a gray background. It had grown colder as well, and I retied the piece of string around my jacket. By now I was exhausted.

It was difficult to lift my feet now, and I was beginning to stumble.

"Can't we sit down for a minute?" I pleaded. "Then we'll have more energy to go on."

"If we sit down, we'll freeze," she said. "We have to keep going."

"I can't keep going. I can't walk any farther," I pleaded.

"Do you know what soldiers do when they can't march any farther?"

"No."

"Of course you do—they sing. Let's sing a marching song. Start a marching song."

I knew a lot of marching songs, but none came to mind, and I didn't feel like singing, anyway. Mother began to sing a soldiers' song that Kiki and I knew. We sang that song through twice, which took my mind off my legs. We sang songs that weren't meant for marching and songs that Mother knew and I learned. I suddenly found us shuffling along a packed-snow road with a group of thatch-roofed cottages clearly outlined against the night sky in front of us. We had finally found the Hungarian village.

The cottages were arranged in rows on both sides of the road. There were no lights in any of the windows, but smoke was rising from all the chimneys.

Mother knocked on the door of the first cottage we came to. She didn't knock politely, but rather pounded with the side of her fist.

A man with a quilt wrapped around his shoulders opened the door and looked quizzically at us.

"We've just come from Poland," Mother said.

I couldn't understand the question he asked in response. It wasn't in Polish, Ukrainian, or Russian.

"Poland," Mother enunciated in Polish, then in Russian. Exhausted, she was leaning with her hand against the door.

A woman came up behind the man, saying something else I couldn't understand. The door opened wider. Mother would have fallen if the man hadn't caught her. The woman supported Mother across the room while the man picked me up off my tired feet. Soon I was sitting on a chair and drinking a warm cup of that same cheesy-tasting milk I had had the night before. The woman was washing Mother's hurt leg. Then I woke up again and it was daylight.

CHAPTER 19

The next morning, two men were standing just inside the front door, talking to Mother. One was a policeman with a large holster in his belt. He had a large, round head and his hair was trimmed close to his scalp.

The other was a civilian, who was shorter than the policeman and somewhat older. He wore something I had never seen before—a shiny leather overcoat. On his head was a green hat with what looked like a little shaving brush stuck in the hatband.

He spoke quietly with Mother for some minutes, then tipped his hat and they left.

"Ah, you're awake, my sleepy hero," Mother said, turning to me.

Mother had on what she had worn yesterday, except that the tear in her stocking had been sewn up with a coarse thread. The woman who had tended to Mother's leg last night stirred a black pot on the stove.

"The police knew right away that we were here," Mother said. I assumed she was speaking to the woman.

"Police," the woman said, nodding. "Hungary police."

"Mr. Vosokos speaks excellent Polish," said Mother, referring to the older of the two men. "He must have lived in Poland at some time."

The woman said something in her language.

Mother asked in Russian if the woman spoke that language.

"No Ruski—Hungarian police," the woman said.

Mother asked if she spoke German.

"No German," the woman said emphatically.

"Thank you." I could tell that Mother had given up on verbal communication and now turned her attention back to me. "You slept well," she said in a jolly tone, and she seemed eager to talk.

I nodded.

"There is a train station here," she said with

excitement. "Soon we will be in Budapest, where we'll stay at a big hotel, like I told you. Here, put these on." She had taken a change of underwear from my backpack, along with a toothbrush. "We just have to stop at the police station to register. Mr. Vosokos couldn't believe that we escaped from the Bolsheviks the way we did."

I saw the woman bring the wooden spoon to her mouth and taste what was in the pot. I hoped it was breakfast, because I was suddenly starving.

Breakfast turned out to be a sweetened, lumpy oatmeal with more of the cheesy milk to drink. We gathered up our belongings and prepared to leave for the police station. As our hostess wiped her hands on her apron, I saw Mother give her some money. The woman pocketed it without interrupting the flow of advice or whatever it was that she was telling us.

Suddenly, I saw Mother put her arms around the woman. "It's thanks to you and your husband that we are alive," she said. "You saved our lives."

As we walked down the snow-covered street. Mother said, laughing, "I know she didn't understand a word I said. But sometimes you just need to talk to someone." I noticed that Mother was walking with less of a limp today. "Would you believe that after all that, I couldn't get to sleep last night?" she said.

I was aware that Mother was speaking differently to me now than she or any grown-up ever had talked to me before. "You know what I'm going to do when we get to America? I'm going to write a book. I thought of it as I was lying there, trying to sleep, and there was no chance of my sleeping after that."

This was the first mention I had heard of us going to America. America was where they made Mickey Mouse cartoons and *Snow White and the Seven Dwarfs*. It was a place where you could buy watches at a pharmacy for only a dollar, and they gave out prizes for having the most freckles. This was exciting news.

The police station was a white frame house on a street that crossed the one we had been on. Among the clay and sod cottages that stood like rows of giant mushrooms, the station looked like something from a bigger town recently dropped into the village.

Mother stopped outside the door and smoothed her hair. Seeing me look at her, she laughed. "I know, I look terrible."

Without her makeup, Mother had dark rings under her eyes that I had never seen before. Her skin was pale, with freckles that I had never known she had, and her eyelashes were so light they were hard to see at all.

"No, you look good," I said. Mother gave her

neckline a little tug down. Realizing what she was doing, she laughed at herself again. "Yulian, we're going to be famous!" she said. "Both of us!" She reached for the door handle.

CHAPTER 20

The police station seemed to be one large room. A low platform held a large desk, behind which sat the policeman we had seen before. In a far corner, behind a little railing, sat Mr. Vosokos. He stood up when we entered and began buttoning his jacket with chubby fingers.

"I thank Missus for coming," he said in excellent, though accented, Polish. He came out from behind his desk and held open a little gate in the railing.

His suit was a double-breasted blue pinstripe with a white shirt and a green tie. On the pinkie of his right hand was a gold ring with a large black stone.

"Sit there," Mother said to me, indicating one of several chairs by the entrance door. She crossed the room and stepped through the little gate, which swung closed behind her. "I am so happy to be back in Hungary," she said to Mr. Vosokos, who held the chair for her. "I have visited your beautiful Budapest a hundred times with my husband."

I saw Mother's fingers instinctively pluck at her skirt to uncover her knee, before encountering the heavy wool of the ankle-length garment. "I don't have a visa, but my passport is in order and, if you call the Polish consul in Budapest, he can arrange for one. He is an old friend of mine, you know, as is the ambassador."

"That will not be necessary," he said with a dismissive wave. "We are all truly amazed at Missus's accomplishment. Missus must be tired. The constable can make Turkish coffee."

I saw Mother's eyebrows flick up at the mention of the coffee. The man said something in Hungarian, and the policeman disappeared through a door in the back.

"The amazing thing is that I am not one bit tired," Mother said. "I am sure it's the excitement, and I will soon collapse." She laughed. "But now I'm just grateful for the chance to talk to an intelligent person.

We've been through so much, and that poor peasant woman speaks nothing but . . . well, I'm not sure what language she spoke. It didn't really sound like the Hungarian one hears in Budapest."

"Yes, one often has a great need to talk after an experience like the one Missus has just had," Mr. Vosokos said. "This region was made a part of the new Czechoslovakia after the Great War, but now it's Hungarian again.

"Two weeks ago, we had three men come across the border," he continued, "but never a woman. The guides, you know, all bring them within sight of the village, then they disappear back into the woods. That undoubtedly is Missus's experience."

"Not exactly. Our guide never even got out of the sleigh."

"The sleigh?"

"He brought us by sleigh within sight of the border. He had bribed the guards, you know, and then he was supposed to carry my son up the mountain, but he just drove off and left us there."

"Unbelievable. There in the snow?"

"Right there in the snow."

"And Missus and her son came all this way by themselves? Incredible!"

Mother nodded her head.

"A woman and a child . . ." the man said. "How did Missus ever find her way?"

"The guide had told us to follow the stream."

"But there is no stream here."

"We followed a stream as far as we could. Then we just stumbled around blind. If we hadn't found this village, purely by chance, we would still be walking—or, more likely, frozen in the snow. God must have been looking out for us. When we got to this village, I didn't know whether we weren't back in Poland."

"Amazing. Just where did Missus cross the border?"

Mother named the village where we had spent the night before. "Somewhere near there," she said. I saw Mr. Vosokos write something down.

Now Mother took the scarf off her head. "I must look awful," she said, laughing and patting her hair with her hand.

"Missus has been through an ordeal."

"I thank Mr. Inspector—or is it Mr. Colonel, perhaps?—on his understanding and congratulate him on his excellent Polish," she said. "He must have lived some years among us."

"I attended university in Warsaw," he said.

"Ah, our beautiful Warsaw—our *once* beautiful Warsaw."

"Ah, yes, what sadness. And I'm afraid it's only

111

Mister. I am just a poor civil servant in the service of his country."

"Mister is being modest. He wears his rank like an impeccably tailored English suit."

"Missus is too kind. But the guide who abandoned Missus so shamefully in the snow after taking her money should be punished. Does Missus happen to remember his name?"

"I believe it was Michael," Mother lied.

"In case we see him here, I will personally see to his punishment. Does Missus remember his last name?"

"They don't use last names."

"Yes, of course."

I wondered why Mother had lied about Yanek's name. He certainly deserved punishment.

"Does Mr. Minister . . ." Mother began. "I mean *Mister*—does Mister happen to be related to General Sir Aubrey Hague?"

"General Hague? I'm afraid I do not know of him. English?"

"Yes, English. And Mister reminds me of the general—younger, of course. I met the general at a reception in the Polish embassy in London last summer. He is not a tall man, but there is no question that he is in command."

Now I knew why Mother was lying. She was trying to flatter the man.

"Perhaps I have some English relations that I did not know about." He laughed.

"Mister Min . . . 'Mister' has such an air of command," Mother said.

"I did serve in the cavalry in the last war," Mr. Vosokos admitted.

"I figured it would be the cavalry. I love the Hungarian cavalry uniforms."

"I was a little thinner then."

"And Mister has such beautiful children."

Mr. Vosokos glanced at the photograph on his desk. "My wife is Austrian."

"She is beautiful."

"She is a skiing champion. She was on the Austrian national ski team."

"Really?"

"Does Missus, or is it Mrs. Baroness, perhaps?" I heard him saying.

Mother laughed. "Just Missus."

"Well, Missus . . ." he began, but was interrupted by the policeman carrying a copper tray. "Ah, the coffee."

On the tray were two cups, a plate of sugar cubes, and a little brass kettle. I could smell the rich coffee aroma across the room.

The policeman presented me with a little tray as well. There was a cup of tea, sugar cubes, milk, and even a lemon slice.

The tea was too hot for me to drink, and I waited for it to cool.

"We traveled three days and nights in the back of my husband's truck," I heard Mother saying.

"And to think that Missus would have to go through an ordeal like this," Mr. Vosokos said. "How did Missus ever find such a guide?"

"Oh, Mister knows, one meets someone at a café, or standing in a line perhaps, who knows someone, who knows someone."

I was getting bored by all this talk. I was looking forward to being in Budapest tonight, in a hotel and ordering dinner. Suddenly, a movement outside the window caught my eye. A sleigh like the one we had ridden in yesterday had pulled into the yard. A bearded old man in peasant clothes covered the horse with a blanket, then saw me looking at him through the window. He came close to the window and broke into a big smile that displayed missing teeth.

I heard him stomp outside the door, and he came in. Passing my chair, he reached down and tickled me before continuing to the back of the room.

"Hey!" I cried in surprise.

The old man turned. I saw the mischievous look on his face and realized he was playing with me. Appreciating the attention, I mimed mock surprise. Mother and Mr. Vosokos both looked at me. I laughed to show that everything was all right. "They were like a comic opera," Mother was saying. "Soviet helmets and red armbands. And, of course, guns. Their leader was even wearing a sword." They both laughed at this.

"Does Mister still have his cavalry sword?"

"I do, indeed. Someday it will be my son's. Of course, they won't be wearing swords when he's in the army."

"Of course," Mother said. "I am interested because when we arrive in America, I will write a book about all this, the Bolsheviks and the Nazis. I have stories about both the Bolshevik and the Nazi zones that the world needs to know about. And Mister will certainly be in it for his kindness."

"Indeed," the man said.

The old man, who had been speaking to the policeman, now sat down on one of the chairs against the side wall, two chairs from mine on my right, crossed his arms over his chest, and closed his eyes. I started to sip some of my tea.

"We had nothing to give our children to eat except carrots," I heard Mother saying. "It was heartbreaking to look at their hungry faces."

I felt myself being watched. Looking up from under my eyebrows, I could see that the old man had turned his face partly to me and had opened just his left eye. The mischievous look was on his face again. I grinned back at him.

"Mister must surely be joking!" Mother suddenly said.

"I deeply wish that I was," the man answered, "but our government has an agreement with the Soviet government in Poland to return all—"

"The Soviet government?"

"Both the Soviet and the German governments."

"But they are invaders. They are not legitimate authorities. Surely the Hungarian government and the rest of Europe are aware. . . ."

"I am truly sorry, Missus, but—"

"I demand to see the Polish consul! I know both him and the ambassador."

"Ah, Missus, I regret that I cannot accommodate that request, either. There is a train to Lwów at 5:23 that Missus and her son will be on. It is quite a comfortable train, and we have no accommodations here for—"

"But we will be shot," Mother said. "The Soviets will take us off the train and shoot us."

"No, Missus. The Soviet authorities—"

Mother stood up. "My son and I did not walk eleven hours through the snow to be put on a train back into Soviet hands!"

"There is nothing I can do. We have our orders."

Now Mother was shouting. "Mister has been giving me coffee and pumping me for information, knowing all along that he was sending us to our deaths!"

"It is only a routine report I have to file—"

"Routine report? My son and I are not one of your routine border incidents. We have walked eleven hours through the snow, risking bullets, risking wolves. . . ."

"There are no more wolves in these woods; the peasants have—"

"Can Mister even look at me when I speak to him?"

Mr. Vosokos was looking down at something he was writing on his desk. He looked up at Mother now. "I am sorry, there is nothing I can do. Missus must not be hysterical. The Soviet government does not shoot civilians."

"Not be hysterical? I have lived five months with the Bolsheviks and—"

"I must ask Missus to sit down now."

"Mister is not inhuman," Mother said in a quieter tone. "He has beautiful children of his own. . . ."

"I am sorry, but I must ask Missus to sit down."

"I have money. . . ."

Mr. Vosokos held up his hand to stop her. "If Missus does not sit down, I will have the constable put her in the cell," he said, looking down at the papers again.

Mother reached under his papers and flung them into the air.

The policeman jumped up and grabbed Mother's arm.

"The cell has no stove," Mr. Vosokos said.

Mother sat down. She was breathing hard.

"Missus must go sit with her son now," Mr. Vosokos said.

The policeman put his hand on Mother's arm again. She stood up and let him lead her to the chair next to mine. Suddenly, she looked tired and much older. As she sat down next to me, I saw tears flowing down Mother's face.

Instinctively, I put my arms around her. "It's all right," I assured her. "Don't cry. Everything will be all right."

"He's secret police," Mother said under her breath.

"What?"

"He's a Nazi. He's trying to make me tell him things. I have nothing to tell him."

"Are the Russians going to shoot us?" I asked. Until a moment ago, I would have been sure the answer was no. Fredek and I had played as spies being stood in front of a brick wall with a blindfold. Now I wasn't so sure.

CHAPTER 21

I could feel Mother pressing her rosary into my hands. "Here, do the Rosary," she was saying.

I could tell from Mother's tone that piety was not the motive behind her order. She had a new plan. I took the rosary and, making the sign of the cross, began whispering the Our Father.

"Louder," Mother said.

I prayed a little louder. Mother joined me at the Hail Mary with a few *la-las* where she didn't remember the words.

I glanced at the old man, who seemed to be

asleep, his arms folded over his chest. I watched the policeman step to the stove to put in more wood. Mr. Vosokos stood up. "I am going home to lunch now," he said. "I will be back. Yoosef will bring Missus some lunch." He put on his leather coat and green hat. The old man stood up as well.

Mother stood up and crossed to meet Mr. Vosokos just outside his railing. She said something I couldn't hear.

"Missus will sit down with her son, or she will wait in the cell!" he said angrily.

Mother sat down again.

I saw the old man purse his lips and secretly shake his head in imitation of Mr. Vosokos, following him to the door.

Through the window, I saw the two men get into the sleigh and, with the old man at the reins and Mr. Vosokos in back, drive away.

Mother leaned her head back against the wall and closed her eyes. I understood it to be no longer necessary to continue praying. At his big desk, the policeman continued writing. "Does Mr. Policeman speak Polish?" Mother asked across the room. Her voice was friendly now. The policeman shook his head. Like Mr. Vosokos, he kept his eyes down on his paperwork.

Mother tried Russian, German, and French with the same results. "Oh come, this close to the border, Mister must certainly understand a *little* Polish," she coaxed. The policeman waved his hand, indicating that he understood a little.

"Is Mister from this village?"

The policeman moved his hand in an arc up from his shoulder and then down to the desk.

"Over the mountain?" Mother asked.

He nodded.

"Is Mister married?"

He nodded again.

"Does Mister have children?"

He held up three fingers. Then he put his index finger to his lips signifying silence. "But why?" Mother asked. "Nobody will know if we speak. And I'm only asking about your children."

The policeman reached back and tapped the wall behind him where the cell must have been. Mother closed her eyes again.

It wasn't long before I saw the old man drive his sleigh back into the space outside the window. He was alone now. He covered the horse again and hung a feed bag over his nose. Then he lifted an iron pot out of the sleigh. As he passed my window, he looked in and winked at me.

The man stamped his feet outside and brought the pot into the police station. He walked across the room and through the door into the back room. The policeman followed him.

"We could run away now," I whispered to Mother. I said it out of a sense of loyalty, but knew it wasn't a realistic plan.

"Hush," Mother said.

The old man came back in, carrying a tray with two steaming bowls and some sliced bread. "Do you speak Polish?" I heard Mother ask the old man as he handed her a bowl. He smiled and nodded his head.

"Do you live in this village?"

He nodded again, handing the other bowl to me. He put the tray with the bread on the chair next to mine and returned to the policeman's desk. The policeman had set two bowls on the desk.

"He doesn't understand a word I said," Mother said.

Our lunch was a meat stew, and it was delicious. Mother didn't want hers and offered it to me, but I was full. The two men talked in low tones as they ate. Mother leaned back against the wall. I thought she might be asleep, but then I saw that her eyes were open, staring at the ceiling.

I must have fallen asleep because the next thing

I knew, Mr. Vosokos was walking across the room to his desk in his leather overcoat. He had a newspaper under his arm.

"I trust Missus's lunch was satisfactory," he said with his back to us as he hung his coat on its hanger.

At first, Mother didn't answer him. "It was very good, thank you," she finally said, even though her bowl was still on the chair next to mine, untouched.

"The constable's wife is an excellent cook," Mr. Vosokos said. He was seated sideways at his desk now, leaning down. I realized he was brushing his shoes.

Through the window, I could see the old man unhitching the horse from the sleigh and leading him somewhere out of sight. Mr. Vosokos was sitting back up in his chair, reading his newspaper. "I would give Missus a newspaper to read," he said across the room, "but they're in Hungarian." Mother didn't answer him.

Then the old man came back past my window and winked at me again. This time, I didn't even try to wink back, waiting for a more opportune time and crossing my fingers in hope.

Coming back into the building, the old man sat down, yawned, and closed his eyes. I waited for him to open one eye and look at me. But he didn't. Time went by, and the old man seemed to be asleep.

Suddenly, his eye popped open. This, I knew was

an opportunity I could not let slip—there might not be another. As he watched me, I forced my left cheek up, closing both eyes, then carefully let the right eye open as far as possible without opening the left. The old man opened his mouth and put his hands to his face in exaggerated surprise. I mimed a laugh, opening my mouth wide and wagging my head left and right. I didn't know whether we really needed to hide our game from Mr. Vosokos, but, somehow, it made it more fun.

Then I remembered the coin in my pocket, the one Mr. Lupicki had given me to practice making it disappear. I drew it out, held it up for the old man to see, pretended to throw it at him, but palmed it instead. The old man raised his hands in pretend fear. I made the coin reappear out of my ear. The old man gripped his head in make-believe amazement.

Suddenly, Mr. Vosokos startled us both as he barked something in Hungarian, and the old man straightened up in his chair. I, too, sat up, as I would have in response to the teacher's command in school. Mother seemed to be sleeping now, but I could see her eyes move from Mr. Vosokos to the old man and then to me.

CHAPTER 22

The policeman stepped down from his platform to switch on an overhead light, and I realized it was growing dark. He nodded to the old man, who got up and went outside.

A few minutes later, he was back outside the window, pushing a wheelbarrow. He stopped at the wagon sleigh and began shoveling something from the wheelbarrow into the sleigh. Steam was rising from it, and it took a minute to realize it was horse manure. He shoveled the manure into a pile in the middle of the wagon sleigh. Then he put the shovel back into the barrow and wheeled it back to wherever he had brought it from.

A few minutes later, he was back again, leading the horse. He led the horse to where the two sleighs stood, turned him around, and backed him between the traces of the wagon sleigh. I could barely see in the fast-growing darkness as he fastened the harness. Then the old man drove the wagon sleigh out of my sight.

In a few minutes, the old man was back inside again. He reported something to the policeman, who went to speak to Mr. Vosokos. Mr. Vosokos said something angry across the room to the old man. The old man shrugged.

"It is time to go to the train station," Mr. Vosokos announced. "I hope Missus will come quietly."

Mother stood up and walked up to the railing again. "I will come quietly, Mr. Minister," she said in a calm voice I could barely hear. "I will also get on that train, but I implore Mister that he send my son to the Polish consul in Budapest."

Suddenly, I felt the blood drain from my face. The idea of separating from Mother now terrified me.

"No, no!" I cried. I rushed to Mother and grabbed her around the waist.

"Yulian, you must be a soldier," Mother scolded.

"You must grow up and come back to fight for Poland."
Then she turned to Mr. Vosokos again. "I implore
you as one parent to another. You have two beautiful
children. Think of them."

Much to my relief, Mr. Vosokos shook his head. "I
cannot help Missus," he said. "I would like to help, but
I can't. I must file my report."

He began putting on his coat. He nodded to the
policeman, who put his hand gently on Mother's
elbow.

"Put your coat on, Yulian," Mother said. I went
back for my coat and knapsack. In a moment we were
all standing in front of the building by the wagon
sleigh. I could smell the manure.

"I have some good news for Missus, at least,"
Mr. Vosokos said. "She will not have to bear the
aggravation of my company any longer. The constable
informs me that the harness on the passenger sleigh is
broken, and he must take this farm sleigh. The sleigh
is not clean, and I am not dressed for such travel at the
moment. I will not accompany Missus and her son to
the station, but will walk home." He tipped his green
hat and began walking carefully through the snow.

The policeman helped Mother into the sleigh. The
old man was already in the sleigh, fixing a spot in the
straw for us to sit at the back.

"The manure is only in the middle," I whispered to Mother. "There isn't any at the way back—we can sit there."

I climbed in after Mother and moved to the back, but saw her move to the front as the policeman settled himself in the single driver's seat.

"Mr. Policeman," Mother said, kneeling behind him in the straw. "Will you take my son to your home—to your wife? I have money and jewels that will make you and your family rich."

I again felt terror at the thought of separation. I could see myself being led by the policeman into a strange house filled with strangers.

I saw Mother tear a button off her jacket and unwrap something, which I knew to be jewelry, and hold it out to the policeman.

The policeman didn't respond. But he didn't say no, as Mr. Vosokos had. He hunched over the reins and clucked the horse into motion.

The sky was clear with a large moon and many stars as we drove through the dark village. Mother continued talking to the policeman, though I couldn't hear her words anymore. The man remained hunched over the reins and seemed unresponsive. The old man sat against the back of the driver's seat and grinned at me. I was in no mood to play games now.

I was again aware this wasn't a game. I had known that all along, but something about this final twist in our journey hadn't seemed real.

Now I knew we were really going back to Poland. The Bolshevik guards would be there at the station, patrolling the platform with their rifles, and they would tell us to put up our hands and arrest us, maybe even shoot us right there.

By this time tomorrow, Mother and I might not exist at all. Fredek, Sonya, the aunts, and Miss Bronia would still be living in the little apartment in Tarnopol, but we'd be gone.

Our trip was not long. The railroad platform, with its roof and electric light, soon appeared before us.

The policeman stopped the horse beside the platform. I wondered how long we would have to wait in the cold for the train. The policeman indicated that we should descend. Mother and I climbed down.

As we stood beside the sleigh, Mother still held her hand out to the policeman. The two men didn't move.

Then the policeman pointed his whip straight over the horse's head, down the train track. "Lwów," he said. It was the first word I had heard him speak. Then he turned to face the rear of the sleigh. He pointed the whip in the opposite direction. "Budapest, seventh hour," he said in broken Polish. Then he made a clucking sound, and the horse moved forward. We watched the sleigh turn and head back toward the village. Suddenly, Mother and I were standing alone beside the empty platform.

We never knew for sure why the policeman and the old man let us go free. Mother was still holding her diamond, so I knew she had not been able to bribe them. Years later, I liked to believe that my making friends with the old man and showing him my disappearing coin trick was the reason. Or maybe it was just that there are caring people everywhere. The train to Lwów came a few minutes later. It stopped, but no one got off or on. We stood on the platform watching the Polish-bound train leave the station.

We stood there shivering until the next train, bound for Budapest, Hungary, roared in with a cloud of steam and a splendid rumble and hiss. We boarded that train.

It was warm inside the train. Mother and I sat facing each other on the plush seats beside the window. I watched the Hungarian countryside fly past us, the moonlight glistening on the crusty snow.

Mother took my hands. I looked directly into her large brown eyes. At that moment, heading for freedom, Mother and I were the only two people in the whole world.

EPILOGUE

Hungary was not the safe haven we had expected.
Hitler and the Nazis were popular in that country.
At the police station, Mother had made the mistake
of telling the security officer that when she got to
America she was going to write a tell-all book about
Nazi and Soviet atrocities. The Hungarian authorities,
we later were told by a friend, were not about to let us
get to America. Mother and I had to go into hiding in
Hungary until we could obtain a visa to Yugoslavia,
which at the time was still a neutral country.

Thanks to Mother's prewar friends throughout

Europe, we managed get visas to make our way from Yugoslavia to Italy to Spain to Portugal and eventually to Brazil. By gradually selling off the diamonds Mother had hidden in her clothes, we paid our way through all those countries.

Our goal was to reach America, where we had relatives. But America had a "quota system," which meant that the United States allowed entry to only so many people from any given country per year. We waited our turn in Rio de Janeiro, Brazil. We landed by ship in New York City in May 1941, eight months before Pearl Harbor.

Mother wrote her book, and it was published in 1942 as *Flight to Freedom*, one of the first stories told about escaping from World War II. I was sent to an American boarding school, where I had trouble learning to read English. At the age of ten, I was learning a skill that my new classmates had learned at the age of six. I still don't read well, but I've found that I have a talent for storytelling.

Thank you for reading my story.

ABOUT THE AUTHOR

Julian Padowicz was a young boy living in Warsaw, Poland, when Nazi Germany invaded and World War II began. He and his mother spent six months surviving under Soviet occupation in southern Poland before escaping over the Carpathian Mountains. Reaching New York in 1941, they became American citizens. Following college, Julian worked for Twentieth Century Fox in Los Angeles and then as a navigator in the U.S. Air Force. After serving in the air force, Julian spent forty years as a documentary filmmaker before retiring to write his memoirs.